LONGMAN LITERATURE

£4.75 h

C000021322

Poems in M, _

Collected by John Agard

 LONGMAN

Longman Literature
Series editor: Roy Blatchford

Novels

Jane Austen   *Pride and Prejudice*   0 582 07720 6
Nina Bawden   *The Real Plato Jones*   0 582 29254 9
Charlotte Brontë   *Jane Eyre*   0 582 07719 2
Emily Brontë   *Wuthering Heights*   0 582 07782 6
Marjorie Darke   *A Question of Courage*   0 582 25395 0
Charles Dickens   *A Christmas Carol*   0 582 23664 9
                  Great Expectations   0 582 07783 4
                  Oliver Twist   0 582 28729 4
Berlie Doherty   *The Snake-stone*   0 582 31764 9
George Eliot   *Silas Marner*   0 582 23662 2
Josephine Feeney   *My Family and Other Natural Disasters*   0 582 29262 X
Anne Fine   *The Book of the Banshee*   0 582 29258 1
            Flour Babies   0 582 29259 X
            Goggle-Eyes   0 582 29260 3
            Madame Doubtfire   0 582 29261 1
            A Pack of Liars   0 582 29257 3
            Step by Wicked Step   0 582 29251 4
F Scott Fitzgerald   *The Great Gatsby*   0 582 06023 0
Graham Greene   *The Captain and the Enemy*   0 582 06024 9
Thomas Hardy   *Far from the Madding Crowd*   0 582 07788 5
               The Mayor of Casterbridge   0 582 22586 8
               Tess of the d'Urbervilles   0 582 09715 0
Susan Hill   *The Mist in the Mirror*   0 582 25399 3
Lesley Howarth   *MapHead*   0 582 29255 7
Aldous Huxley   *Brave New World*   0 582 06016 8
Robin Jenkins   *The Cone-Gatherers*   0 582 06017 6
Joan Lindsay   *Picnic at Hanging Rock*   0 582 08174 2
Joan Lingard   *Night Fires*   0 582 31967 6
Bernard MacLaverty   *Lamb*   0 582 06557 7
Michelle Magorian   *Goodnight Mister Tom*   0 582 31965 X
Jan Mark   *The Hillingdon Fox*   0 582 25985 1
Dalene Matthee   *Fiela's Child*   0 582 28732 4
Beverley Naidoo   *Journey to Jo'burg*   0 582 25402 7
George Orwell   *Animal Farm*   0 582 06010 9
Alan Paton   *Cry, the Beloved Country*   0 582 07787 7
Ruth Prawer Jhabvala   *Heat and Dust*   0 582 25398 5
Catherine Sefton   *Along a Lonely Road*   0 582 29256 5
Robert Swindells   *A Serpent's Tooth*   0 582 31966 8
                   Daz 4 Zoe   0 582 30243 9
                   Follow a Shadow   0 582 31968 4
Anne Tyler   *A Slipping-Down Life*   0 582 29247 6
Robert Westall   *Urn Burial*   0 582 31964 1
Edith Wharton   *Ethan Frome*   0 582 30244 7

Other titles in the Longman Literature series are listed on page 182.

Contents

3 Rap Boasts Rants 43

1 Lend the Poem Your Breath

To start off this book of 'performance poetry' I have selected a few of my poems to say something about the way I perform them in schools, festivals or wherever. Here is one I wrote and first performed at Poetry Carnival, a week of poetry celebrations in Brent in 1985.

Poetry Jump-Up

Tell me if ah seeing right
Take a look down de street

Words dancin
words dancin
till dey sweat
words like fishes
jumpin out a net
words wild and free
joinin de poetry revelry
words back to back
words belly to belly

Come on everybody
come and join de poetry band
dis is poetry carnival
dis is poetry bacchanal
when inspiration call
take yu pen in yu hand
if yu dont have a pen
take yu pencil in yu hand
if yu don't have a pencil
what the hell
so long de feeling start to swell
just shout de poem out

Words jumpin off de page
tell me if Ah seein right
words like birds
jumpin out a cage
take a look down de street
words shakin dey waist

2

words shakin dey bum
words wit black skin
words wit white skin
words wit brown skin
words wit no skin at all
words huggin up words
an saying I want to be a poem today
rhyme or no rhyme
I is a poem today
I mean to have a good time

Words feeling hot hot hot
big words feeling hot hot hot
lil words feeling hot hot hot
even sad words cant help
tappin dey toe
to de riddum of de poetry band

Dis is poetry carnival
dis is poetry bacchanal
so come on everybody
join de celebration
all yu need is plenty perspiration
an a little inspiration
plenty perspiration
an a little inspiration

Jump-Up is an expression used to describe exuberant
calypso-style dancing, as seen for instance in the streets
at carnival. Around the time I wrote the poem, there was
a popular Soca song by the St Kitts' singer, Arrow, with the
catchy chorus 'Feeling Hot Hot Hot ...' (if you get a chance to
hear the record you won't forget the beat of that chorus). Well,
when I come to the part of the poem that says
'big words feeling hot hot hot/lil words feeling hot hot hot ...'
I echo the same rhythm of that chorus.

Think of a carnival scene with its mingling colours and sounds,
and as part of that scene think of a band of words, costumes
and all, a celebration of the spoken word and the written word.

It's always intriguing how an ordinary expression may suddenly spark off a poem. A headmaster from the north of England once told me that he found it rather amusing when an English person asks politely 'How do you do?' and is answered with another polite question 'How do you do?'. As a result of that headmaster's comment the expression 'How do you do?' started to float around in my imagination. The expression soon took the form of a plant that thrives on politeness.

The howdooyoodoo

Haven't you heard
of the how-doo-yoo-doo
how-doo-yoo-doo?

I'm surprised
you haven't heard
of the how-doo-yoo-doo
how-doo-yoo-doo

Spend a day or two
in a place called England
and I'm sure you'll meet
the how-doo-yoo-doo
how-doo-yoo-doo

But for those of you
without a clue
the how-doo-yoo-doo
is a creeping kind of plant
that takes you by the hand
and says how-doo-yoo-doo
how-doo-yoo-doo

And if by chance
you should say
I'm feeling down today
I got a tumour in my brain

and my old grandmother
keeps haemorrhaging
drops of rain
that doctors can't restrain

Then the how-doo-yoo-doo
gets embarrassed
almost a fright
retreats into itself
and begins to wither

So upon meeting
the how-doo-yoo-doo
this most peculiar plant
don't be alarmed
be polite
just take it by the hand
and say how-doo-yoo-doo
how-doo-yoo-doo
how-doo-yoo-doo
how-doo-yoo-dooooooooooooooooooo

Before I perform this poem I ask the audience to join with me in the how-doo-yoo-doo chorus while shaking hands with one another. Maybe you can have fun doing an impression of a naturalist introducing the how-doo-yoo-doo plant.

Audience participation is an integral part of oral culture whether we think of story-telling, worksongs, or the liturgy of the church with the priest chanting and the congregation answering back.

While growing up in Guyana, I attended Roman Catholic schools, and at my secondary school, St Stanislaus, most of our teachers were Jesuit priests. I used to serve at mass as an altar boy, and sometimes draped a sheet over my shoulders pretending to be a priest while my cousin knelt with a glass of wine we had pinched from my uncle. Maybe by pretending to be a priest I was responding to the sense of drama and ritual and language in the same way that I liked to make up cricket commentaries pretending to be the famous commentator, John Arlott.

'Prayer to Laughter' is a poem from my book *Laughter is an Egg*, a collection in which I explore laughter as a divine trickster-egg which brings a crack to sad faces. With the audience repeating line by line after me, 'Prayer to Laughter' offers an opportunity to create the feeling of a congregation playfully invoking the compassion of this egg.

Prayer to Laughter

O Laughter
giver of relaxed mouths

you who rule our belly with tickles
you who come when not called
you who can embarrass us at times

send us stitches in our sides
shake us till the water reaches our eyes
buckle our knees till we cannot stand

we whose faces are grim and shattered
we whose hearts are no longer hearty
O Laughter we beg you

crack us up
crack us up

The world of mythology is a marvellous source of nourishment and inspiration to poets and very often a poem can take on a story-telling voice. The poem following puts on the magic cloak of fable or parable and in this cloak there are pockets of surprises. So let's gather closer around the fire of our imagination...

Once Upon a Time

Once upon a time there lived
a small joke
in the middle of nowhere.

This small joke
was dying to share
itself with someone

but nobody came to hear
this small joke.

So this small joke told itself
to the birds

and the birds told this small joke to the trees
and the trees told this small joke to the rivers
and the rivers told this small joke to the mountains
and the mountains told this small joke to the stars

till the whole world
started to swell with laughter

and nobody believed
it all began
with a small joke

that lived in the middle of nowhere.

Everybody kept saying

it was me
it was me.

Just as stories take us back to our early oral beginnings, so, too,
does music. There was a time when recitation and singing were
seen as one, and ballad, remember, had its birth in dance.
Music has inspired many a poet, and poetry has inspired many a
musician.

The growth of steelband music inspired me to write a cycle of poems, 'Man to Pan'. Steelband has a remarkable history, especially when you consider how a steelpan or steel drum, said to be the only musical instrument invented for the twentieth century, first grew out of an old oil drum in Trinidad. To begin with, the oil drum must be sunk to a concave shape with a sledge hammer, heated over a fire, notes grooved with a chisel – a process which is reflected in the next poem as well as the jubilation and the pain which is part of steelband history. If your school doesn't have a steelpan, why not ask your music teacher to introduce one? The inside of the steelpan with its radiating segments will remind you of a spider's web.

Web of Sound

is the sinking

of metal

is the cleaving

of a feeling

is the weaving

of a dream

is the sounding

of a scream

is the drumming

of a heart

is the grounding

of a hurt

is the pounding

of a rage

is the wounding

of a night

is the grooving

of blackness

is the moving

of a man

of pan

for the taste of fire

to the thrust of chisel

in a web of sound

in old oildrum

to a beat of steel

to tones of blood

to tunes of love

by slash of stars

by trickles of light

to the embrace

The chant, with its spell-like repetition, has cast a magic on the imagination of poets down the ages. Here is that tricky Laughter again breaking into a chant, and while saying the poem out loud, you can imagine Laughter disguised as a mysterious but mischievous wise woman or magician.

Laughter's Chant

HA-HA-HA-E-E-E-O
HA-HA-HA-E-E-E-O
HA-HA-HA-E-E-E-O
IN SUNRISE
IN MOONGLOW
I COME I GO
NOW YOU HEAR ME
NOW YOU DON'T.

HA-HA-HA-E-E-E-O
HA-HA-HA-E-E-E-O
HA-HA-HA-E-E-E-O
FROM WIND I COME
TO WIND I GO
IN YOUR EYES
I MAKE RAIN
IN YOUR EYES
I MAKE RAIN.

HA-HA-HA-E-E-E-O
HA-HA-HA-E-E-E-O
HA-HA-HA-E-E-E-O
THUNDER I MAKE ROAR
AT THE DOOR
OF YOUR MOUTH
THUNDER I MAKE ROAR
AT THE DOOR
OF YOUR MOUTH.

HA-HA-HA-E-E-E-O
HA-HA-HA-E-E-E-O
HA-HA-HA-E-E-E-O
ALL RIGHT SAD FACE
I WILL COME AGAIN
TO WRINKLE YOUR NOSE.

I hope this anthology gives you as much pleasure as it has given me putting it together. Lend the poem your breath and the poem will lend you its voice. Bring your body language/ evoke/invoke/provoke/remember/before there was writing people spoke.

Let me end by thanking the poets for the gift of their voices.

2 Belongings with a Beat

Track Suit

two-tone stretch nylon yellow stripes on navy blue
I got a brand new track suit I got the old one too
I got the old one too

I got a new track suit
I wear it every day
keeps me cool and casual
I wore yesterday
I wore it yesterday

I got a new track suit
I wear it everywhere
track me down to the training ground
maybe i'll be there
maybe i'll be there

wearing the brand new track suit
medicine ball to boot
knee pads an airline bag
and the overall smell of brut
the overall smell of fruit

expert eyes have scrutinized
and scientists agree
one track suit would suffice
but you're better off with three
you're better off with three

two-tone stretch nylon yellow stripes on navy blue
i got a brand new track suit I got the old one too
I got the old 1 . . . 2

John Cooper Clark
England

MY BAG
to Cecil Taylor

MY BAG IS HERE IT IS JUST MY SIZE
MY BAG IS DEEP AND DARK SO DONT
BE TOO SMART I HAVE MY BAG
IT IS ALL MY OWN AND I AND I ALONE
KNOWS WHAT IS HAPPENING IN MY BAG
MY BAG IS WARM SOMETIMES HOT BUT HIP
MY BAG IS NOTHING MORE THAN MY BAG
THUS IT MAY JUST BE TOO DAMN HEAVY
FOR YOU TO WORRY OR TRY TO CARRY BUT
DONT GET UPSET AND SCARY ITS MY BAG
I KNOW MY BAG CAUSE IT IS MY BAG
I KNOW EXACTLY WHERE ITS AT MY BAG

Ted Joans
African-American

The War God's Horse Song

I am the Turquoise Woman's son

On top of Belted Mountain beautiful horses
slim like a weasel

My horse has a hoof like striped agate
his fetlock is like fine eagle plume
his legs are like quick lightning

My horse's body is like an eagle-feathered arrow

My horse has a tail like a trailing black cloud

I put flexible goods on my horse's back

The Holy Wind blows through his mane
his mane is made of rainbows

My horse's ears are made of round corn

My horse's eyes are made of stars

My horse's head is made of mixed waters
        (from the holy waters)
        (he never knows thirst)

My horse's teeth are made of white shell

The long rainbow is in his mouth for a bridle
with it I guide him

When my horse neighs
different-colored horses follow

When my horse neighs
different-colored sheep follow
I am wealthy from my horse

Before me peaceful
Behind me peaceful
Under me peaceful
Over me peaceful
Around me peaceful
Peaceful voice when he neighs
I am everlasting and peaceful
I stand for my horse

Traditional Navajo

Spell to Summon the Owner of the Shoes

Here are your shoes.

I have mended them with strong thread
I have mended them with all my skill
I have mended them with tough leather
I have mended them with fine leather.

These shoes cannot be worn by anyone
Not by my friends who are barefoot
Not by my friends with lovely faces
Not by the deserving.

It's not a question of eyes or shoulders
It's not a question of images
It's not a question of name or promises
These shoes are for your feet and none other.

May you wear them to shreds
May you wear them to tatters
May you wear holes in them
May you wear them till there is nothing left of them

May you cross mountains in them
May you cross cities in them
May you cross moors in them
May you cross fields in them

May you wear them in hot weather
May you wear them in wet weather
May you wear them through snow and ice
May you wear them through mud and slush

May you wear them on grass
May you wear them on concrete
May you wear them on carpeted floors
May you wear them in good company

May you wear them at night
May you wear them to dance in
May you work in them without aching feet
May you be forever without corns and blisters.

Without you these shoes are useless
Without you they are worthless
Without you they are not special
Without you they are emptiness and clutter

Come and get them.

Jeni Couzyn
South Africa/UK

Money moans

Money I haven't got enough
Money I'll never have enough
Money is what I want, I want
Money so that I don't have to worry about

Money When you have lots of
Money you can make lots more
Money by doing nothing but letting your
Money work for you by making

Money breeds
Money leads to
Money leads to
Money leads to worrying about

Money makes holes in trouser pockets
Money makes guns and nuclear rockets
Money makes hospitals and tanks
Money makes funeral parlours and banks
Money makes people go off the rails
Money fills coffers, coffins and jails

I lie awake at night
Worrying about *money*
A taxperson somewhere
Spends all the days
Making lots of   *money*
Finding new ways
To keep me awake at night
Worrying about   *money*

Mone mone money
All I do is moan
about money.

Roger McGough
England

Leaflets

Leaflets, leaflets, I like leaflets,
I love leaflets when they're free.
When I see a pile of leaflets,
I take one, or two (or three).

Banks are always good for leaflets –
They've got lots of leaflets there –
Leaflets on investing money:
How to be a Millionaire.

And I go to my Gas Show Room,
For their leaflets are such fun,
And I visit travel agents –
They've got leaflets by the ton.

Leaflets, leaflets, I like leaflets,
I love leaflets when they're free.
When I see a pile of leaflets,
Something strange comes over me.

Theatre foyers offer leaflets:
What to see and how to book.
Stations, libraries and so on –
All have leaflets if you look.

I've got leaflets by the dozen,
I've got leaflets by the score,
I've got leaflets by the hundred,
Yet I always yearn for more.

Colin West
England

Madam

Madam
I have sold you
an electric plug
an electric torch
an electric blanket
an electric bell
an electric cooker
an electric kettle
an electric fan
an electric iron
an electric drier
an electric mixer
an electric washer
an electric peeler
an electric sweeper
an electric mower
an electric singer
an electric knife
an electric clock
an electric switch
an electric toothbrush
an electric razor
an electric teapot
an electric eye
an electric light.
Allow me to sell you
an electric chair.

Christopher Logue
England

The Car

The car with a cracked windshield.
The car that threw a rod.
The car without brakes.
The car with a faulty U-joint.
The car with a hole in its radiator.
The car I picked peaches for.
The car with a cracked block.
The car with no reverse gear.
The car I traded for a bicycle.
The car with steering problems.
The car with no back seat.
The car with the torn front seat.
The car that burned oil.
The car with rotten hoses.
The car that left the restaurant without paying.
The car with bald tires.
The car with no heater or defroster.
The car with its front end out of alignment.
The car the child threw up in.
The car *I* threw up in.
The car with the broken water pump.
The car whose timing gear was shot.
The car with a blown head-gasket.
The car I left on the side of the road.
The car that leaked carbon monoxide.
The car with a sticky carburetor.
The car that hit the dog and kept going.
The car with a hole in its muffler.
The car with no muffler.
The car my daughter wrecked.
The car with the twice-rebuilt engine.
The car with the corroded battery cables.

The car bought with a bad check.
Car of my sleepless nights.
The car with a stuck thermostat.
The car whose engine caught fire.
The car with no headlights.
The car with a broken fan belt.
The car with wipers that wouldn't work.
The car I gave away.
The car with transmission trouble.
The car I washed my hands of.
The car I struck with a hammer.
The car with payments that couldn't be met.
The repossessed car.
The car whose clutch-pin broke.
The car waiting on the back lot.
The car of my dreams.
My car.

Raymond Carver
USA

Ladders

Beep! from the street – a rusty van,
Standing beside it a tall thin man:
'Ladders!

Ladders wobbly, ladders steady,
Ladders for trees when plums are ready,
Ladders!

Ladders new, ladders old,
Ladders for painting ceilings gold,
Ladders!

Ladders narrow, ladders wide,
Ladders for lofts with ghosts inside,
Ladders!

Ladders short, ladders tall,
Ladders for scaling a palace wall,
Ladders!

Ladders for saving skaters who
Braved thin ice and plunged right through,
Ladders to take you out of Monday
Back into bed on a lazy Sunday,
Ladders!

Ladders silver, ladders brown,
Ladders for climbing out of town,
Up past chimneys, up so high,
Higher than clouds or an eagle's eye,
Till, five miles beneath your feet,
You see in a tiny winding street
The tiny figure of a tall thin man
Who stands and shouts by a rusty van:
Ladders!'

Richard Edwards
England

Zoe's Ear-rings

She bought 'em in the autumn
After spotting 'em in Nottingham.
She took 'em home to Cookham
And she put 'em in a drawer

Till May came and the day came
When she wore 'em down to Shoreham,
But *nobody* was for 'em
So she wore 'em nevermore …

Till the wedding of her sister
To a mister out at Bicester,
Name of Jimmy, who said, '*Gimme*,'
So without 'em she went home,

But she nipped back down to nick 'em
For a knees-up in High Wycombe,
For an evening quite near Chevening
And a dawn at Kilmacolm.

They were in 'er for a dinner
Which was excellent, in Pinner,
And another one, a cracker,
In Majacca – that's in Spain –

Then she popped 'em on in Haddenham
And didn't feel too bad in 'em:
She felt in 'em in Cheltenham,
Just as right as rain.

They looked smart on in Dumbarton,
They looked wizard on the Lizard,
They looked corking down in Dorking
And incredible in Crewe.

When she wore 'em into Rugely
They impressed the people hugely,

While in Fordham folk adored 'em,
And they *loved* 'em in West Looe!

The citizens of Kettering
Had never seen a better ring,
In fact no better pair of 'em –
'Take care of 'em!' they cried.

Then she slithered into Lytham with 'em,
Shaking out a rhythm with 'em,
Wobb-er-ling and jogg-er-ling
Her head from side to side.

Folk in Preston thought the best 'un
Was the right 'un. In New Brighton
And in Sefton, though, the *left* 'un
Was the one they favoured more,

While in Greenham, when they'd seen 'em,
They said, 'How to choose between 'em?
What one praises in its brother,
In the *other* one is for!'

Then she tried 'em with new make-up
On a sponsored run round Bacup,
And at Norwich for a porridge-
Eating contest which she won,

But, spilling 'em in Gillingham,
Her lobes felt light in Willingham,
And nothing else is filling 'em,
So now

The poem's

Done!

Kit Wright
England

A Child's Christmas in Cardiff

I WANT A BMX BIKE!
I WANT A BMX BIKE!
I WANT A BMX BIKE!

An' it's Christmas morning
An' guess wha'?

I GORRA BMX BIKE!
I GORRA REAL BMX BIKE!
I GORRA BMX BIKE!

An' the first thing I does on it
Is take it out the lane
An' do a FANTASTIC WHEELIE
An' fall OFF
An' land on my bum!
An' hurt myself
An' cry
WAAAAAAAAAAAAAAAAAAAAAAAAAAAAAAAAAAAAAAAA!
An' Mummy comes and gets me
WAAAAAAAAAAAAAAAAAAAAAAAAAAAAAAAAAAAAAAAA!
An' carries me back in the house
WAAAAAAAAAAAAAAAAAAAAAAAAAAAAAAAAAAAAAAAA!
An' cuddles me
WAAAAAAAAAAAAAAAAAAAAAAAAAAAAAAAAAAAAAAAA!
An' kisses me better
                    Yuck!
An' now
        I gorra BMX bike
                For sale.

Christopher Mills
Wales

28

If I Had a Hundred Hats

If I had a hundred hats on my head
a hundred hats   a hundred colors
a hundred hats   a hundred colors and shades of colors
a hundred hats   a rain of colors

if I had a hundred hats on my head
I'd go into the market place
clear me a way to the market place
and toss them in happiness

if I had a hundred hats on my head
I'd go into the market place
and everybody would clear me a way
and wait for my waving the hats

if I had a hundred hats on my head
a hundred hats   a hundred colors and shades of colors
if I had a hundred hats   and a high sun going
straight to my head   straight to my colors

oh the crowd   ready to shout its cry of praise
its great heart thumping in the square
heart of the crowd waiting

for the waving of a hundred hats   a hundred
                          colors and shades

Amir Gilboa
Israel

Give me a House

Give me a house, said Polly.
Give me land, said Hugh.
Give me the moon, said Sadie.
Give me the sun, said Sue.

Give me a horse, said Rollo.
Give me a hound, said Joe.
Give me fine linen, said Sarah.
Give me silk, said Flo.

Give me a mountain, said Kirsty.
Give me a valley, said Jim.
Give me a river, said Dodo.
Give me the sky, said Tim.

Give me the ocean, said Adam.
Give me a ship, said Hal.
Give me a kingdom, said Rory.
Give me a crown, said Sal.

Give me gold, said Peter.
Give me silver, said Paul.
Give me love, said Jenny,
Or nothing at all.

Charles Causley
England

Tattoo

(dedicated to Micky Sharpz Lewis)

Micky's an artist y'know,
He puts his pictures in my skin,
I carry them around for ever
Better than gold in my pockets.
Tattoo artist, him,
Brighter than a flash
He draws in my flesh with his needles.
I pay for his art with more than money
I give him my blood and pain.
You who look down on us
And call us tattooed savages,
Who despise us and sneer,
Safe in your money and your fear,
Who write a cheque
For a marble statuette
You give nothing, and get nothing.
But when we sit
And feel the needles burn
We're proud.
We get something no one can
Ever take away from us.
However else you humble us,
However else you try
To rob us of our dignity,
We'll always have our pictures to tell us
We've got something
You'd never dare to own.
Oh yes, Micky's an artist right enough,
His paintings in my skin give me pride
and fair exchange is no robbery to us.

Joolz
England

31

Chair Affair

the chair bites me. angrily i kick it

the chair wheezes every time
i sit down on it

i have decided i hate this chair
even though i need its support

the chair moves into an awkward angle every
time i get up so i am forced to look at it
before i sit down again

hard little round metallic doo-doos
keep coming out of the chair
causing me to watch my step

i have offered a truce. the loss of 25
pounds. the chair scoffs

the chair doctor states it will take
3 months and over four thousand dollars to
cure the chair

today my horoscope said avoid
recalcitrant chairs

when i came in from lunch
i found another butt in my chair

'chairs are the true plague of mankind'
– Chairman Mao

Wanda Coleman
African-American

A Peach Dress

blue and white day
and a peach dress
oh and a cuddly black
smooth black and brown and white dog
and a white cat
and his one blue eye
and his one green eye
and waking up to the
purr purr purr
of blackie
deep among the sheets

bok clack whirr
against the wall
i am billy jean king
i know them all
white dresses and all
dresses i cut them
from paper
and hang them on dolls
white with golden stars
midnight blue pale pink
and a lime green

i will marry in lime green
like a wild nymph
fresh from the fields
still damp
i will marry my only only
i will dance for you daddy
one two three and a
one two three and a
ballet bounce and a twirl
and a purr purr
pirouette

Maíghréad Meebh
Ireland

Night Mail

I
This is the Night Mail crossing the border,
Bringing the cheque and the postal order,

Letters for the rich, letters for the poor,
The shop at the corner, the girl next door.

Pulling up Beattock, a steady climb:
The gradient's against her, but she's on time.

Past cotton-grass and moorland boulder,
Shovelling white steam over her shoulder,

Snorting noisily, she passes
Silent miles of wind-bent grasses.

Birds turn their heads as she approaches,
Stare from bushes at her black-faced coaches.

Sheep-dogs cannot turn her course;
They slumber on with paws across.

In the farm she passes no one wakes,
But a jug in a bedroom gently shakes.

II
Dawn freshens, the climb is done.
Down towards Glasgow she descends,
Towards the steam tugs yelping down the glade of cranes,
Towards the fields of apparatus, the furnaces
Set on the dark plain like gigantic chessmen.
All Scotland waits for her:
In the dark glens, beside pale-green lochs
Men long for news.

III
Letters of thanks, letters from banks,
Letters of joy from girl and boy,
Receipted bills and invitations
To inspect new stock or visit relations,
And applications for situations,
And timid lovers' declarations,
And gossip, gossip from all the nations,
News circumstantial, news financial,
Letters with holiday snaps to enlarge in,
Letters with faces scrawled on the margin,
Letters from uncles, cousins and aunts,
Letters to Scotland from the South of France,
Letters of condolence to Highlands and Lowlands,
Written on paper of every hue,
The pink, the violet, the white and the blue,
The chatty, the catty, the boring, the adoring,
The cold and official and the heart's outpouring,
Clever, stupid, short and long,
The typed and printed and the spelt all wrong.

IV
Thousands are still asleep,
Dreaming of terrifying monsters
Or a friendly tea beside the band at Cranston's or Crawford's:
Asleep in working Glasgow, asleep in well-set Edinburgh,
Asleep in granite Aberdeen,
They continue their dreams,
And shall wake soon and long for letters,
And none will hear the postman's knock
Without a quickening of the heart,
For who can hear and feel himself forgotten?

W. H. Auden
England

35

Computer Game

WHAM! WHAM! Zappa zappa!
Zappa zappa zoom!
There's a manic computer game
up in my room.

As soon as I switch off
the lamp every night
enemy space ships
appear on the right:

ZOOP-ZOOP! ZOOP-ZOOP!
Beep-beep-beep.
The noises it makes
stop me going to sleep.

Now as the main
invasion fleet nears
I snug in my pillow
with plugs in my ears.

ZAPOW! ZAP! ZAP-ZAP!
ZAP! POW-POW!
As you may have guessed,
I'm wideawake now.

Zip-zip! Zeep-zeep!
Zip! BAM-BAM!
The rockets rush,
the lasers slam,

the deck guns splat,
the ray guns blast,
each invader explodes
as it rushes past.

Bip-bip, bip-bip,
zeep-zeep ZAM!
Just one to go – look out!
BAM! BAM!

My ship is moving
in the deep.
Beep-beep, beep-beep,
beep beep beep.

The sky is black,
my ship is steady;
I open my eyes –
it's morning already!

Charles Thomson
England

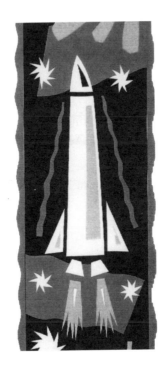

I am a purse ...

I am a purse
               lying on the road,
alone here in broad daylight.
You don't even see me, people.
                       Your feet
walk over and around me.
And don't you
               understand anything?
And don't you, really,
               have eyes?
That dust,
          that you raise yourselves,
conceals me,
          so clever
             of you.
Look more closely.
             Only a glance is needed.
I'll give everything to you,
               all that I treasured.
And don't look for my owner.
I laid myself on the ground.
Don't think
          they'll suddenly pull a string,
and above the crooked fence not far away
you'll see some little Nina,
saying with a laugh:
             'They fooled you!'

Don't let a humiliating laugh and some faces
in a window somewhere scare you.
I'm no fraud.
           I'm the real thing.
Just look inside me!
I'm afraid of one thing,
                to your disfavor:
that right now,
          in broad daylight,
I won't see
        the one I wait for,
that the one who should
              won't pick me up.

Yevgeny Yevtushenko
Russia

39

The Glassy Green and Maroon

Cinderella had glass slippers
I used to believe in because
my mother has always worn
glass bangles of a special kind –
made as I thought from similar glass.

Ma's bangles are thick maroon and dark,
they are green glints and unbreakable
      I think
because she can wear them all day:
whether she scrubs out clothes
or dishes, the glass bangles stay on.
Afraid of ruining her gold wedding bangles
she somehow trusts the glassy green
and maroon. Every day, broom in hand
she sweeps out the dust
from the verandah, from our doorsteps,
while the glass bangles catch
the morning sun, the afternoon sun …

Then finally, when she raises her arms
to undo the scarf protecting her hair,
how the glass bangles glisten, loyal
    year after year
above her small wrists – bands of lingering light
illuminating her
who would otherwise remain hidden
with her work.

Nowadays I can't find
such sturdy bangles – not in Ahmedabad,
not in Delhi. The glass snaps
like raw spaghetti, like dry twigs
from termite emptied trees,
like rusty barbed wire,
rusty tin shack neighbourhoods
where tin roofs creak against their crookedness
break against the slightest movement
from the wind, from a dog's tail, from a child
                         who walks out the door.
The glass snaps
the bangles break.

Sujata Bhatt
India/Germany

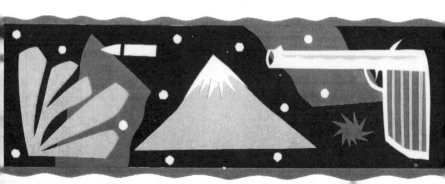

3 Raps Boasts Rants

Bawd

I'll get all dolled up in my gladrags, stay
up till all hours, oh
up to no good.
It'll amaze you, the company I keep –
and I'll keep them at arm's length –
I've hauled my heart in off my sleeve.

I'll let my hair down,
go blonde, be a bombshell, be on the make,
I'll gold-dig, I'll be frankly fake.

I'll paint my face up, paint the town,
have carmine nails, oh
be fatal dame.
I've bold eyes, kohl sockets.
I'll look daggers, kill.
My lipstick colour's Merry Hell.

I'd frighten the French.
I'll be a torment, haunt men's dreams,
I'll wear my stockings black with seams.

I'll rouge my cleavage, flaunt myself, my heels
will be perilously high, oh
but I won't sway.
I'll shrug everything off the shoulder,
make wisecracks, be witty off the cuff.
Tell blue jokes in mixed company.

I'll be a bad lot.
I've a brass neck. There is mayhem in my smile.
No one will guess it's not my style.

Liz Lochhead
Scotland

The First

I'd be the first to climb Mount Eiger on a tiger
The first to swim the Channel inside out
The first to run amok in thirty seconds
And train on boiled black pudding, peas and stout.

I'd be the first to win the Ladies' Open Doubles
At Wimbledon, at tennis, on my own
The first to catch a haggis single-handed
And keep it in a cage till fully grown.

I'd be the first to surf Downunder underwater
On the belly of a person-eating shark
Compose a piano fugue for few good reasons
Go on telly then impersonating Bach.

I'd be the first to rollerskate and reach the South Pole
South Polar bears all marvelling at my skill
The first to hang-glide all the way to Venus
And get back quick (because it's all downhill).

I'd be the first to leapfrog over Blackpool Tower
Clear Grand Canyon in one almighty leap.
Dream about the FA Cup at Wembley
Score the winning goal while walking in my sleep.

I'd be the first in all these things
So it's sad to reveal
That maybe now I'm past it
Though they say you're as young as you feel.

Roger McGough (87½)
England

45

O, that I were the son of Andriamanitra!

O, that I were the son of Andriamanitra!
I would ascend to the sky;
I would marry the daughter of a king;
I would eat the ripe fruit of ferns;
I would dig stone borders;
I would tie *horondrano* fruit together.
– I am the *horondrano*, so you rend me.
If you rend me, then I am in the earth.
– If you were in the earth, would I not dig you out?
– If you dig me out, I am in the sky.
– If you were in the sky, would I not climb up?
– If you climb up, I am in a rock.
– If you were in a rock, would I not break you?
– If you break me, I am in a leaf.
– If you were in a leaf, would I not shake you off?
– If you shake me off, I am in a tree.
– If you were in a tree, would I not cut you down?
– If you cut me down, I belong to another.
– If you belonged to another, I would give you up very easily.

Traditional Madagascar

I am a girl who loves to shoot

I am a girl who loves to shoot,
I love the feathered fowl and brute,
I love them with a love as strong
As ever there came from heaven down.

Why should I not love them living as dead?
As I shoot, as I shoot, and as my fine dog Tray
Brings the shot one to hand, he is I, I am they.
Oh why do my friends think this love is so questionable?
They say they love animals but they do not love them as I
        am able,
Seeing them run and fly and letting them run, fly and die,
I love them to distraction as the wild wind goes by,
As the rain and the storm on this wide upper hill,
Oh no one loves the animals as I do or so well.
If I am not hungry I let them run free,
And if I am hungry they are my darling passionate delicacy.
Into the wild woods I go over the high mountain to the valley
        low,
And the animals are safe; if I am not hungry they may run
        and go,
And I bless their beautiful appearance and their fleetness,
And I feel no contradiction or contriteness.
I love them living and I love them dead with a quick blood
        spurt
And I may put them in the pot and eat them up with a loving
        heart.

I am a girl who loves to shoot,
I love the feathered fowl and brute,
I love them with as great a love
As ever came down from heaven above.

Stevie Smith
England

Rogan the Lion's Roaring Song

You've seen me on golden syrup tins
And movies by MGM
I appeared with a witch and a wardrobe
And I didn't think much of them
I'm an aristocrat and a gentleman
I never blow bubble gum
And I talk real posh, for I never say gosh
Or belly or blimey or bum

> I go ROAR
> That's right royal roaring
> I go ROAR
> It never gets boring
> My ROAR
> My wonderful roar
> I go ROAR
> I roar like a river
> I go ROAR
> And my enemies shiver
> At my ROAR
> My wonderful super-charged roar

Now I had a job in a circus once
And I didn't care much for that
For they didn't treat me like a king
But a musclebound pussy cat
Now I'm not so young as I used to was
But you'd better not forget
Though my teeth are falling and my mane is balding
There's life in the old lion yet

> I go ROAR
> That's right royal roaring
> I go ROAR
> It never gets boring
> My ROAR
> My wonderful roar
> I go ROAR

I roar like a river
I go ROAR
And my enemies shiver
At my ROAR
My wonderful super-charged ROAR

I used to go zebra-bashing
Or take a little deer for lunch
But now I'd rather be given a tin
Of Kit-e-Kat or Whiskas to munch
But I haven't given up slaughtering
I murder now and again
I might bite in half some young giraffe
And you'll know I'm still in business when

I go ROAR
That's right royal roaring
I go ROAR
It never gets boring
My ROAR
My wonderful ROAR
I go ROAR
I roar like a river
I go ROAR
And my enemies shiver
At my ROAR
My wonderful super-charged walloping
thatchery
ROOOOOOOOOAR!

Adrian Mitchell
England

Baby-K Rap Rhyme

My name is Baby-K
An dis is my rhyme
Sit back folks
While I rap my mind;

Ah rocking with my homegirl,
My Mommy
Ah rocking with my homeboy,
My Daddy
My big sister, Les an
My Granny,
Hey dere people – my posse
I'm the business
The ruler of the nursery

poop po-doop
poop-poop po-doop
poop po-doop
poop-poop po-doop

Well, ah soaking up de rhythm
Ah drinking up my tea
Ah bouncing an ah rocking
On my Mommy knee
So happy man so happy

poop po-doop
poop-poop po-doop
poop po-doop
poop-poop po-doop

Wish my rhyme wasn't hard
Wish my rhyme wasn't rough
But sometimes, people
You got to be tough

Cause dey pumping up de chickens

Dey stumping down de trees
Dey messing up de ozones
Dey messing up de seas

Baby-K say, stop dis –
please, please, please

poop po-doop
poop-poop po-doop
poop po-doop
poop-poop po-doop

Now am splashing in de bath
With my rubber duck
Who don't like dis rhyme
Kiss my baby-foot
Babies everywhere
Join a Babyhood

Cause dey hotting up de globe, man
Dey hitting down de seals
Dey killing off de ellyies
For dere ivories
Baby-K say, stop dis –
please, please, please

poop po-doop
poop-poop po-doop
poop po-doop
poop-poop po-doop

Dis is my Baby-K rap
But it's a kinda plea
what kinda world
Dey going to leave fuh me?
What kinda world
Dey going to leave fuh me?
    Poop po-doop.

Grace Nichols
Guyana/UK

The Michael Rosen Rap

You may think I'm happy, you may think I'm sad,
You may think I'm crazy, you may think I'm mad,
But hang on to your seats and listen right here
I'm gonna tell you something that'll burn your ear.

A hip. Hop. A hip hop hap.
I'm givin' you all the Michael Rosen rap.

I was born on the seventh of May
I remember very well that awful day
I was in my mother, curled up tight
Though I have to say, it was dark as night.
Nothing to do, didn't have to breathe,
I was so happy, didn't want to leave.

Suddenly, I hear some people give a shout:
One push, Mrs Rosen, and he'll be out.
I'm tellin' you all, that was a puzzle to me,
I shouted out, 'How do you know I'm a "he"'?
The doctor shouted, 'Good Lord, he can talk.'
I popped out my head, said, 'Now watch me walk.'
I juked and jived around that room,
Balam bam boola, balam de ditty boom.

A hip. Hop. A hip hop hap.
I'm givin' you all the Michael Rosen rap.

When I was one, I swam the English Channel,
When I was two, I ate a soapy flannel,
When I was three, I started getting thinner,
When I was four, I ate the dog's dinner,
When I was five, I was in a band playing drums,
When I was six, I ate a bag of rotten plums,
When I was seven, I robbed a bank with my sister,
When I was eight, I became Prime Minister,
When I was nine, I closed all the schools,
When I was ten, they made me King of the Fools.

So that's what I am, that's what I be
With an M, with an I, with a K, with an E.
That's what I am, that's what I be
Mr Mike, Mr Michael, Mr Rosen, Mr Mr.
A hip. Hop. A hip hop hap.
I'm givin' you all the Michael Rosen rap.

Michael Rosen
England

Overstanding

Open up yu mind mek some riddim cum in
Open up yu brain do some reasoning
Open up yu thoughts so we can connect
Open up fe knowledge an intellect,
Open up de speaker mek we blast de sound
Open up de sky mek de Bass cum down
Open up yu eyes mek we look inside
If yu need fe overstand dis open wide.

Open up yu house mek de Refugee cum in
Yu may overstand an start helping
Open yu imagination, gu fe a ride
If yu want fe overstand dis open wide

Open up yu fiss an welcum a kiss
Getta loada dis open up business
Open up yu Bank Account an spend
Open up yu wallet an check a fren,
Open up de dance floor mek I dance
Open up yu body an luv romance
If yu have not opened up, yu hav not tried
See de other side an open wide

Open up de border free up de land
Open up de books in de Vatican
Open up yu self to any possibility
Open up yu heart an yu mentality,
Open any door dat yu confront
Let me put it straight, sincere and blunt
Narrow mindedness mus run an hide
Fe a shot of overstanding
Open Wide.

Benjamin Zephaniah
Jamaica/UK

The Complete Alternative History of the World, Part One

I'm not your Little Woman
I'm not your Better Half
I'm not your nudge, your snigger
Or your belly laugh.

I'm not Jezebel
And I'm not Delilah
I'm not Mary Magdalen
Or the Virgin Mary either.

Not a Novice or a Nun
Nor a Hooker or a Stripper
Not Super Shirley Conran
Not Jill the Ripper.

No I'm no Scissor-Lady –
I won't snip at your . . . locks.
I'm not a siren, you're not obliged
To get off my rocks.

Not Medusa, not Medea
And, though my tongue may be salty,
I'm not the Delphic sybil –
Or Sybil Fawlty.

I'm not Poison Ivy
You can throw away the lotion
I'm not your Living Doll
I'm not Poetry In Motion.

And if selling Booze and Cars
Involves my body being used, well . . .
I'm not Queen Victoria
But I'm not amused.

And if you don't like my Body
You can sodding well lump it –
I'm not a Tart-with-a-Golden-Heart
Or Thinking Man's Crumpet.

I'm not your Woman of Achievement
Not your Slimmer of the Year
I'm not Princess Diana …
No Frog Princes 'ere!

I'm not little Ms Midler
I'm not little Miss Muffet
Make me An Offer I Can't Refuse –
And I'll tell you to stuff it!

'Cos I'm not your Little Woman
I'm not your Lady Wife
I'm not your Old Bag
Or the Love of Your Life –

No, I'm not your Little Woman
Not your Better Half
I'm not your Nudge, your Snigger
Or your Belly Laugh.

Liz Lochhead
Scotland

The Mystery

I am the wind which breathes upon the sea,
I am the wave of the ocean,
I am the murmur of the billows,
I am the ox of the seven combats,
I am the vulture upon the rocks,
I am a beam of the sun,
I am the fairest of plants,
I am a wild boar in valour,
I am a salmon in the water,
I am a lake in the plain,
I am a word of science,
I am the point of the lance of battle,
I am the God who created in the head of the fire.
Who is it who throws light into the meeting on the mountain?
Who announces the ages of the moon?
Who teaches the place where couches the sun?
(If not I)

Traditional Celtic

Riddle Song

On the tree and in the tree
under rivulets of raven rain.
On the tree and in the tree
I climb the pain and down again.
On the tree and in the tree
raven's beak is in my eye.
so tell me who am I?
so tell me who am I?

I am the saxon and the jew
so tell me who am I?
I am the many and the few
so tell me who am I?
I am the one, I am the three
so tell me who am I?
I am the man I am the tree
so tell me who am I?
so tell me who am I?

I am the hive, I am the bee
so tell me who am I?
I am the river, rain and sea
so tell me who am I?
I am the three, I am the nine
so tell me who am I?
I am the bread, I am the wine
so tell me who am I?
so tell me who am I?

Bill Lewis
England

58

The Blank Generation
(A new slant on an age-old theme)

The youth of today don't know they're born
... at the age of five, they're mowing the lawn

By the time they're eight, their golden dream
is a foolproof, high-yield pension scheme

As puberty strikes, know where they are?
Out there on Sundays, washing the car

Birthdays and Christmas, the same old cry:
'Please, please, Mum, can I have a new tie?'

Games: 'You be a company director,
I'll be the local tax inspector.'

Teenage rebellion: 'Grow up, Dad,
and buy a suit, you look real sad!'

Music: Doors and Rolling Stones (!)
and bleepy acid monotones*

(* though some are really daring creatures –
they like Blur and the Manic Street Preachers)

Politics: Grey. A tinge of green
from time to time, to suit the scene.

Ideals? 'Er ... well ... to earn a wage,
and quickly attain middle age.

Changing the world? For god's sake, no!
Our parents tried that years ago!'

        *   *   *

I see no need to mince my words.
Hey, get a life, you boring nerds!

Attila The Stockbroker
England   59

Machoman

I ain't no SCHWARZENEGGER
Or a CLAUDE VAN DAMME
Ain't a BRONSON or a RAMBO
Or a ROBOCOP man
I don't have ripplin biceps
An oozi or a nine
Or plant the seeds of bad behaviour
Firmly in my mind
Don't like the virtue of obsession
Pickin on the weak
Although I'm wise, and know what's happenin
Down there on the street
I don't like people walkin round
Thinking drugs are cool
When CRACK, COCAINE and HEROIN
Is just a game fer fools
An attitude of mind I hate
I see so much, it's SLACK
When access is denied to me
Because my skin is BLACK
I see them in the ghetto streets
Actin out the violence
That takes away the breath of life
Leaving blood and silence
Too many times, we stand and watch
Observe and stand and stare
Because we just don't give a damn
An option not to care
Alarms that deafen all our ears
Can never stop the thief
The tears I see, and cries I hear
The anguish and the grief
Of those whose loved ones snatched away

Hear the screams and moans
Of victims of the joyrider
The crunch of broken bones
I cry inside with deep despair
Which quickly turns to rage
When the target for a mugger
Is defenceless, and elders age
I watch those eager to prove themselves
Following the trail
Leading to the space in hell
Your own apartment, JAIL
So smile away, behave so bad
Put malice in your head
Being macho ain't a virtue
When prematurely dead

Martin Glynn
UK

The Boast of the Good Farmer

I have ploughed and I have sweated,
And now I am enjoying my crops, my friends,
Like the bushbuck which uses its tail to push rice-plants
        into its mouth
As a sign of its contentment.

Good farming wins respect, my friends.
Where I drink beer now
I drink to my heart's content:
When I eat my food
I eat with a settled heart,
Like our little friend the fish
Which makes white soup for us,
Which plays in its pool all day
Without anything to trouble its heart.

A farmer is a king:
Even the wizard pays homage to you.

Farming brings honour, my friends:
You need not trail your feet to beg at the homes of junior men.

You see me in my prosperity today
Because during the rains I am the friend of the mud:
Rather, I attack the soil with my special friend, the hoe.

    Fancy not cultivating!
    Fancy not hoeing!
    Fancy not cultivating!
      Take the little hoe and break the soil!

    The day when I killed a partridge,
    When the child's mother had gone to the field,
    The porridge ran into my mouth like lightning.
      Take the little hoe and weed the soil!

Traditional Zimbabwe

Party Man

I am a laughing sea-lion,
I thread the needle of your desire,
my dark, dimpled chin
breaks open like a fruit
to the white of my teeth:
the seeds of promise.

I am a red bow-tie,
I carry the song,
my tongue rasps and lilts,
tickles the ice in glasses;

I am a dancing sailor,
wind in your ear,
the spray from my lips
arcs towards you.

I am a blind pebble,
in the whirlpool,
swilling and falling
I drop to the depths
of dreamless roundness:
oblivion.

Katie Donovan
Ireland

Prayer Before Birth

I am not yet born; O hear me.
Let not the bloodsucking bat or the rat or the stoat or the
    club-footed ghoul come near me.

I am not yet born, console me.
I fear that the human race may with tall walls wall me,
        with strong drugs dope me, with wise lies lure me,
            on black racks rack me, in blood-baths roll me.

I am not yet born; provide me
With water to dandle me, grass to grow for me, trees to talk
        to me, sky to sing to me, birds and a white light
            in the back of my mind to guide me.

I am not yet born; forgive me
For the sins that in me the world shall commit, my words
        when they speak me, my thoughts when they think me,
            my treason engendered by traitors beyond me,
                my life when they murder by means of my
                    hands, my death when they live me.

I am not yet born; rehearse me
In the parts I must play and the cues I must take when
        old men lecture me, bureaucrats hector me, mountains
            frown at me, lovers laugh at me, the white
                waves call me to folly and the desert calls
                    me to doom and the beggar refuses
                        my gift and my children curse me.

I am not yet born; O hear me,
Let not the man who is beast or who thinks he is God
      come near me.

I am not yet born; O fill me
With strength against those who would freeze my
      humanity, would dragoon me into a lethal automaton,
         would make me a cog in a machine, a thing with
            one face, a thing, and against all those
               who would dissipate my entirety, would
                  blow me like thistledown hither and
                     thither or hither and thither
                        like water held in the
                           hands would spill me.

Let them not make me a stone and let them not spill me.
Otherwise kill me.

Louis MacNeice
Ireland

Masters of War

Come you masters of war
You that build all the guns
You that build the death planes
You that build the big bombs
You that hide behind walls
You that hide behind desks
I just want you to know
I can see through your masks

You that never done nothin'
But build to destroy
You play with my world
Like it's your little toy
You put a gun in my hand
And you hide from my eyes
And you turn and run farther
When the fast bullets fly

Like Judas of old
You lie and deceive
A world war can be won
You want me to believe
But I see through your eyes
I see through your brain
Like I see through the water
That runs down my drain

You fasten the triggers
For the others to fire
Then you sit back and watch
When the death count gets higher
You hide in your mansion
As young people's blood
Flows out of their bodies
And is buried in the mud

You've thrown the worst fear
That can ever be hurled
Fear to bring children
Into the world
For threatenin' my baby
Unborn and unnamed
You ain't worth the blood
That runs in your veins

How much do I know
To talk out of turn
You might say that I'm young
You might say I'm unlearned
But there's one thing I know
Though I'm younger than you
Even Jesus would never
Forgive what you do

Let me ask you one question
Is your money that good
Will it buy you forgiveness
Do you think that it could
I think you will find
When your death takes its toll
All the money you made
Will never buy back your soul

And I hope that you die
And your death'll come soon
I will follow your casket
In the pale afternoon
And I'll watch while you're lowered
Down to your death bed
And I'll stand o'er your grave
'Till I'm sure that you're dead

Bob Dylan
USA

4 Monologues Dialogues Dialtones

The party to which you were not invited

'… was like no other party before.
What a party.
What a party.
Everyone was there.
Well, everyone, that is, but you.
It was incredible.
Amazing.
You wouldn't believe what went on.
I mean let's face it if you weren't at that party
then you don't know what PARTY means.
What a party.
You just couldn't imagine a party like that.
There'll never be a party like it again.
Everyone's still talking about it.
Well, everyone, that is, but you.
A party like that can change your life.
I mean any other party
is going to seem drab now in comparison.
I mean, I've been to parties with a capital P
but this was a party with a capital PARTY
know what I mean?
No. I don't suppose you do.
What a party.
A party like that comes once in a lifetime, maybe.
Still at least everyone can share the memory
well, everyone, that is, …'

Henry Normal
UK

New Baby

My baby brother makes so much noise
that the Rottweiler next door
phoned up to complain.

My baby brother makes so much noise
that all the big green frogs
came out the drains.

My baby brother makes so much noise
that the rats and the mice
wore headphones.

My baby brother makes so much noise
that I can't ask my mum a question,
so much noise that sometimes

I think of sitting the cat on top of him
in his pretty little cot with all his teddies.
But even the cat is terrified of his cries.

So I have devised a plan. A soundproof room.
A telephone to talk to my mum.
A small lift to receive food and toys.

Thing is, it will cost a fortune.
The other thing is, the frogs have gone.
It's not bad now. Not that I like him or anything.

Jackie Kay
Nigeria/Scotland

My Dad

I love to watch my dad
when he's cutting his toenails.
My dad does not mind
if he has an audience.
He is like a medical TV show
during a tricky operation.
He says, 'First you trim the nail
leaving a strip of white at the top
before probing under the nail for crud.'
The crud is all different colours
because it is fluff from his socks.
He cannot understand people
who think that's all there is
to cutting your nails.
Neither can I.
Next he wedges a tiny pair of silver scissors
into the corner and takes another scissors
and goes clip, clip, clip.
That's for ingrown toenails.
To polish things off,
he scrapes the sides of his nail
with a little file just in case.
I would like to be as skilled
as my dad at cutting toenails
in the years to come.

Julie O'Callaghan
USA/Ireland

The Voyeur

what's your favourite word dearie
is it wee
I hope it's wee
wee's such a nice wee word
like a wee hairy dog
with two wee eyes
such a nice wee word to play with dearie
you can say it quickly
with a wee smile
and a wee glance to the side
or you can say it slowly dearie
with your mouth a wee bit open
and a wee sigh dearie
a wee sigh
put your wee head on my shoulder dearie
oh my
a great wee word
and Scottish
it makes you proud

Tom Leonard
Scotland

Don't ask me

Don't ask me
Who won the first Marathon
I am not interested in sport

Don't ask me
Who dropped the first nuclear bomb
That is not my problem

Don't ask me
Who painted the Mona Lisa
I don't care for Art

Don't ask me
Who got the Nobel prize in literature this year
I am not paid for that

Don't ask me
Who wrote the ninth symphony
Music doesn't move me.

Don't ask me
Who first set foot on the moon
I couldn't care less.

Don't ask me
Who murdered Julius Caesar
It is no concern of mine

Don't ask me
I have no time for stupid things
I have my job to do
And my family to care for
About anything else
I don't give a damn.

Jon Milos
Yugoslavia

Small-town Sunday

Well, shall we go?
Yeh come on, let's go.
Any action round here?
No, no action round here.
Barman, a beer!
It's dead in here.
This summer's been cold.
And we're getting old.
Kate's did a roast.
Here, it's nearly half past.
Come on then, let's go.
Yeh come on, let's go.
Is he in tonight?
Yeh, he's in tonight.
Shall we go in?
OK, let's go in.
Watching telly tonight?
Yeh, it's my telly night.
Anything on?
Yeh, there's something on.
Got any cash?
Yeh, I got some cash.
Fancy a half?
Yeh well, just a half.
Well, shall we go?
Yeh, come on, let's go.
Watching telly tonight?

Yeh, it's my telly night.

Wolf Bierman
Germany

Boy

I liked being small. When I'm on my own
I'm small. I put my pyjamas on
and hum to myself. I like doing that.

What I don't like is being large, you know,
grown-up. Just like that. Whoosh. Hairy.
I think of myself as a boy. Safe slippers.

The world is terror. Small you can go *As I*
lay down my head to sleep, I pray … I remember
my three wishes sucked up a chimney of flame.

I can do it though. There was an older woman
who gave me a bath. She was joking, of course,
but I wasn't. I said *Mummy* to her. Off-guard.

Now it's a question of getting the wording right
for the Lonely Hearts verse. There must be someone
out there who's kind to boys. Even if they grew.

Carol Ann Duffy
UK

Parrot

I said, 'I love you.'
You answered, 'I love you.'
I said, 'I hate you.'
You answered, 'I hate you.'
I said, 'Shall we separate now?'
You answered, 'Shall we separate now?'
Always, always,
You were a parrot.
It was all because you repeated my words exactly
That we came to separate.

Kazuko Shiraishi
Japan

The Lesson

I'll tell you what now little brother
I'm going to teach you something
you'll never ever forget.

You go half way upstairs that's right.
You turn round you shut your eyes.
You keep them shut tight.

Now on the count of five
now I want you to jump.
Now is that clear.

Don't be scared little brother.
I'll be standing at the bottom here
to catch you so be brave.

1 … 2 … 3 … 4 …

Five I said I'd teach you something
this is it don't ever trust anybody.
When you're older you'll thank me for it.

Shut up.

Brian McCabe
Scotland

Phone Booth

Someone is loose in Moscow who won't stop
Ringing my phone.
Whoever-it-is listens, then hangs up.
Dial tone.

What do you want? A bushel of rhymes or so?
An autograph? A bone?
Hello?
Dial tone.

Someone's lucky number, for all I know,
Is the same, worse luck, as my own.
Hello!
Dial tone.

Or perhaps it's an angel calling collect
To invite me to God's throne.
Damn, I've been disconnected.
Dial tone.

Or is it my old conscience, my power of choice
To which I've grown
A stranger, and which no longer knows my voice?
Dial tone.

Are you standing there in some subway station, stiff
And hatless in the cold,
With your finger stuck in the dial as if
In a ring of gold?

And is there, outside the booth, a desperate throng
Tapping its coins on the glass, chafing its hands,
Like a line of people who have been waiting long
To be measured for wedding-bands?

I hear you breathe and blow into some remote
Mouthpiece, and as you exhale
The lapels of my coat
Flutter like pennants in a gale.

Speak up, friend! Are you deaf and dumb as a stone?
Dial tone.

The planet's communications are broken.
I'm tired of saying hello.
My questions might as well be unspoken.
Into the void my answers go.

Thrown together, together
With you, with you unknown.
Hello. Hello. Hello there.
Dial tone. Dial tone. Dial tone.

Andrei Voznesensky
Russia

What Is This In Reference To? *or*
We Must Get Together Sometime Soon!

Hello.
I'm sorry.
I can't talk to you.
I am unavailable.
I am out of the house.
I am out of town.
I am out of the country.
I am out of my mind.
I am indisposed.
The cat has my tongue.
Please do not hang up.
I know this is frustrating
                ridiculous
                solipsistic
                inconvenient
                mechanical
                and
                a pain in the ass
Please listen for the beep.
When you hear the beep
please leave a message as long as you like
or better still
please leave a brief message
or better yet
state your purpose in concise
readily decipherable terms and be sure
to leave your name your number

the time
the date
the place
and a list of the secret desires underlying this conventional
even hackneyed outreach represented
by
your call.
This is your dime.
Listen for the beep.
Sucker.

June Jordan
African-American

Wife Who Smashed Television Gets Jail

'She came home, my Lord, and smashed in the television;
Me and the kids were peaceably watching *Kojak*
When she marched into the living room and declared
That if I didn't turn off the television immediately
She'd put her boot through the screen;
I didn't turn it off, so instead she turned it off –
I remember the moment exactly because Kojak
After shooting a dame with the same name as my wife
Snarled at the corpse – Goodnight, Queen Maeve –
And then she took off her boots and smashed in the television;
I had to bring the kids round to my mother's place;
We got there just before the finish of *Kojak;*
(My mother has a fondness for *Kojak*, my Lord);
When I returned home my wife had deposited
What was left of the television into the dustbin,
Saying – I didn't get married to a television
And I don't see why my kids or anybody else's kids
Should have a television for a father or mother,
We'd be much better off all down in the pub talking
Or playing bar-billiards –
Whereupon she disappeared off back down again to the pub.'
Justice O'Brádaigh said wives who preferred bar-billiards to
    family television
Were a threat to the family which was the basic unit of society
As indeed the television itself could be said to be a basic unit of
    the family
And when as in this case wives expressed their preference in
    forms of violence
Jail was the only place for them. Leave to appeal was refused.

Paul Durcan
Ireland

A Many-Splendoured Doughnut

The optimist: It's a round pastry,
the pessimist: It's just a hole,
the dualist: Both are quite tasty,
the animist: Thanks to its soul.

The chemist: Carbons and sugars,
the physicist: Atoms and space,
the dentist: Decaying molars,
the evangelist: Edible grace.

The analyst: Oral regressive,
the behaviourist: Hunger response,
the pragmatist: Calories excessive,
the fatalist: Try it but once.

The capitalist: Mouthful of profit,
the marxist: Capitalist greed!
the hedonist: Junk food and scoff it,
the egotist: Just what I need.

The symbolist: Ring of great power,
the cubist: A circular square,
the realist: A thing to devour,
the impressionist: Light, shadow, air!

The idealist: Halo in batter,
the platonist: Great Sugared Roll!
the materialist: What does it matter?
the monist: A part of the whole.

The existentialist: Well-fried in being,
the moralist: Sweet as a sin,
the determinist: Can't help agreeing,
the sophist: Where does it begin?

Norman Silver
England

School

The Teacher
What maiden will marry
the wind?

The Child
The maiden of all
our desires.

The Teacher
What does the wind
give the maiden?

The Child
Whirlwinds of gold.
A pileup of maps.

The Teacher
And she gives him what?

The Child
Her heart laid bare.

The Teacher
Tell me her name.

The Child
Her name is a secret.

> (The window
> in the school
> has a curtain
> of stars.)

Federico Garcia Lorca
Spain

Ballade

I know flies in milk
I know the man by his clothes
I know fair weather from foul
I know the apple by the tree
I know the tree when I see the sap
I know when all is one
I know who labors and who loafs
I know everything but myself.

I know the coat by the collar
I know the monk by the cowl
I know the master by the servant
I know the nun by the veil
I know when a hustler rattles on
I know fools raised on whipped cream
I know the wine by the barrel
I know everything but myself.

I know the horse and the mule
I know their loads and their limits
I know Beatrice and Belle
I know the beads that count and add
I know nightmare and sleep
I know the Bohemians' error
I know the power of Rome
I know everything but myself.

Prince I know all things
I know the rosy-cheeked and the pale
I know Death who devours all
I know everything but myself.

François Villon
France 15th century

Mum Takes a Bath

On a normal, average day in our house:

Tracey and Darren
  are fighting with Sharon,
the TV set's blaring,
  and Gran's started swearing,
the cat caught his paw
  when Michelle slammed the door
and he's rowling and yowling in pain;
once again, baby Shane's
  stuck his hand down the drain
and he can't get his thumb out
  so he's screaming his lungs out:
the shrill accusations
  and reverberations
of the whole pandemonium's mass aggravations
  are shaking the house from the roof to
    foundations –

I go to the bathroom
  and lock myself in.

I go to the bathroom
  and shut out the din.
I go to the bathroom and turn on the taps.
  And I peel them all off like a skin.

Because
  in the water
    the warm, silky water
      the deep, soothing water
with my ears under water
I can't
      hear
          a thing …

Mick Gowar
England

About Friends

The good thing about friends
is not having to finish sentences.

I sat a whole summer afternoon with my friend once
on a river bank, bashing heels on the baked mud
and watching the small chunks slide into the water
and listening to them – plop plop plop.
He said 'I like the twigs when they ... you know ...
like that.' I said 'There's that branch ...'
We both said 'Mmmm.' The river flowed and flowed
and there were lots of butterflies, that afternoon.

I first thought there was a sad thing about friends
when we met twenty years later.
We both talked hundreds of sentences,
taking care to finish all we said,
and explain it all very carefully,
as if we'd been discovered in places
we should not be, and were somehow ashamed.

I understood then what the river meant by flowing.

Brian Jones
UK

Leaves

Who's killed the leaves?
Me, says the apple, I've killed them all.
Fat as a bomb or a cannonball
I've killed the leaves.

Who sees them drop?
Me, says the pear, they will leave me all bare
So all the people can point and stare.
I see them drop.

Who'll catch their blood?
Me, me, me, says the marrow, the marrow.
I'll get so rotund that they'll need a wheelbarrow.
I'll catch their blood.

Who'll make their shroud?
Me, says the swallow, there's just time enough
Before I must pack all my spools and be off.
I'll make their shroud.

Who'll dig their grave?
Me, says the river, with the power of the clouds
A brown deep grave I'll dig under my floods.
I'll dig their grave.

Who'll be their parson?
Me, says the Crow, for it is well-known
I study the bible right down to the bone.
I'll be their parson.

Who'll be chief mourner?
Me, says the wind, I will cry through the grass
The people will pale and go cold when I pass.
I'll be chief mourner.

Who'll carry the coffin?
Me, says the sunset, the whole world will weep
To see me lower it into the deep.
I'll carry the coffin.

Who'll sing a psalm?
Me, says the tractor, with my gear grinding glottle
I'll plough up the stubble and sing through my throttle.
I'll sing the psalm.

Who'll toll the bell?
Me, says the robin, my song in October
Will tell the still gardens the leaves are over.
I'll toll the bell.

Ted Hughes
England

Weather Rapport

Sorry we can't bring you
the WEATHER RAPPORT
because the WEATHER ain't
gonna be what we thought,
What will happen
from week to week?
I don't know
because the WEATHER is doing the FREAK!

We don't know WHETHER
the sun will shine
we don't know WHETHER
there'll be a hurricane
we don't know WHETHER
we'll get sleet or snow
we don't know WHETHER
there'll be a shower of rain
we don't know WHETHER
fog will show its face
we don't know WHETHER
the frost will take hold
we don't know WHETHER
temperatures will soar
we don't know WHETHER
it will just stay cold.

The snow starts to fall
through the sunshine
the rain begins to dance
at the same time,
The wind starts to blow
creating a song
a confused state of affairs
the WEATHER has gone wrong

Then man plays part
and makes things worse
all because he wants
to fatten his purse.
And that RAPS up
our RAPPORT for this week,
the outlook is
the WEATHER'S still doing the FREAK!

Levi Tafari
Jamaica/UK

Who's There?

Who's there?
Who's that hiding behind the brown trees,
lurking among the green undergrowth of the woodland?
It's us – the Tree-Elves and the Moss-People
and we are watching you
breaking branches without permission.

Who's there?
Who's that gliding over the wet rocks,
dancing and splashing at the sea's edge?
It's us – the Rock Sirens and Mer-Men
and we are watching you pouring poison in our watery home.

Who's there?
Who's that drifting through the sparkling mist,
flying across bright skies, bursting out of clouds?
It's us – the Alven, we who travel in bubbles of air
and we are watching you filling our palace of sky with dust and dirt.

Who's there?
Who's that running over mountains,
wading through cold rivers, striding over forests?
It's us – the Kelpies and Glashans,
the powerful beasts of the wiser world
and we are watching you
wasting these waters and hurting this land.

John Rice
Scotland

Message

Pick up the phone before it is too late
And dial my number. There's no time to spare –
Love is already turning into hate
And very soon I'll start to look elsewhere.

Good, old-fashioned men like you are rare –
You want to get to know me at a rate
That's guaranteed to drive me to despair.
Pick up the phone before it is too late.

Well, wouldn't it be nice to consummate
Our friendship while we've still got teeth and hair?
Just bear in mind that you are forty-eight
And dial my number. There's no time to spare.

Another kamikaze love affair?
No chance. This time I'll have to learn to wait
But one more day is more than I can bear –
Love is already turning into hate.

Of course, my friends say I exaggerate
And dramatize a lot. That may be fair
But it is no fun being in this state
And very soon I'll start to look elsewhere.

I know you like me but I wouldn't dare
Ring you again. Instead I'll concentrate
On sending thought-waves through the London air
And, if they reach you, please don't hesitate –
Pick up the phone.

Wendy Cope
England

93

Market Women's Cries

Apples

Come buy my fine wares,
Plums, apples, and pears.
A hundred a penny,
In conscience too many:
Come, will you have any?
My children are seven,
I wish them in Heaven;
My husband's a sot,
With his pipe and his pot,
Not a farthing will gain them,
And I must maintain them.

Asparagus

Ripe 'sparagras
Fit for lad or lass,
To make their water pass:
O, 'tis pretty picking
With a tender chicken!

Onions

Come, follow me by the smell,
Here are delicate onions to sell;
I promise to use you well.
They make the blood warmer,
You'll feed like a farmer;
For this is every cook's opinion,
No savoury dish without an onion;
But, lest your kissing should be spoil'd,
Your onions must be thoroughly boil'd:
Or else you may spare
Your mistress a share,
The secret will never be known:
She cannot discover
The breath of her lover,
But think it as sweet as her own.

Oysters

Charming oysters I cry:
My masters, come buy,
So plump and so fresh,
So sweet is their flesh,
No Colchester oyster
Is sweeter and moister:
Your stomach they settle,
And rouse up your mettle;
They'll make you a dad
Of a lass or a lad;
And madam your wife
They'll please to the life;
Be she barren, be she old,
Be she slut, or be she scold,
Eat my oysters, and lie near her,
She'll be fruitful, never fear her.

Herrings

Be not sparing,
Leave off swearing.
Fresh from Malahide,
Better never was tried.
Come, eat 'em with pure fresh butter and mustard,
Their bellies are soft, and as white as a custard.
Come, sixpence a-dozen, to get me some bread,
Or, like my own herrings, I soon shall be dead.

Oranges

Come buy my fine oranges, sauce for your veal,
And charming, when squeezed in a pot of brown ale;
Well roasted, with sugar and wine in a cup,
They'll make a sweet bishop when gentlefolks sup.

Jonathan Swift
Ireland 17th/18th century

Granny in de Market Place

Yuh fish fresh?

Woman, why yuh holdin' meh fish up tuh yuh nose?
De fish fresh. Ah say it fresh. Ah ehn go say it any mo'

Hmmm, well if dis fish fresh den is I who dead an' gone
De ting smell like it take a bath in a lavatory in town
It here so long it happy. Look how de mout' laughin' at we
De eye turn up to heaven like it want tuh know 'e fate
Dey say it does take a good week before dey reach dat state

Yuh mango ripe?

Gran'ma, stop feelin' and squeezin' up meh fruit!
Yuh ehn playin' in no ban'. Meh mango eh no concertina

Ah tell yuh dis mango hard just like yuh face
One bite an' ah sure tuh break both ah meh plate
If you cahn tell de difference between green an' rosy red
dohn clim' jus' wait until dey fall down from de tree
Yuh go know dey ripe when de lizard an dem start tuh feed
but dohn bring yuh force-ripe fruit tuh try an' sell in here
it ehn burglars is crooks like all yuh poor people have to fear

De yam good?

Old lady, get yuh nails outta meh yam!
Ah mad tuh make yuh buy it now yuh damage it so bad

Dis yam look like de one dat did come off ah de ark
She brother in de Botanical Gardens up dey by Queens Park
Tourists with dey camera comin' from all over de worl'
takin' pictures dey never hear any yam could be dat ole
Ah have a crutch an' a rocking-chair someone give meh fuh free
If ah did know ah would ah bring dem an' leave dem here fuh she

De bush clean?

Well, I never hear more! Old woman, is watch yuh watching meh young
young dasheen leaf wit' de dew still shinin' on dem!

It seem tuh me like dey does like tuh lie out in de sun
jus' tuh make sure dat dey get dey edges nice an' brown
an' maybe is weight dey liftin' tuh make dem look so tough
Dey wan' build up dey strength fuh when tings start gettin' rough
Is callaloo ah makin' but ah 'fraid tings go get too hot
Yuh bush go want tuh fight an' meh crab go jump outta de pot

How much a poun' yuh fig?

Ah have a big big sign tellin' yuh how much it cos'
Yuh either blin' yuh dotish or yuh jus' cahn read at all

Well, ah wearing meh glasses so ah readin' yuh big big sign
but tuh tell yuh de trut' ah jus' cahn believe meh eye
Ah lookin' ah seein' but no man could be so blasted bol'
Yuh mus' tink dis is Fort Knox yuh sellin' fig as if is gol'
Dey should put all ah all yuh somewhere nice an' safe
If dey ehn close Sing-Sing prison dat go be the bestest place

De orange sweet?

Ma, it eh hah orange in dis market as sweet as ah does sell
It like de sun, it taste like sugar an' it juicy as well

Yuh know, boy, what yuh sayin' have a sorta ring
De las' time ah buy yuh tell meh exactly de same ting
When ah suck ah fin' all ah dem sour as hell
De dentures drop out an' meh two gum start tuh swell
Meh mout' so sore ah cahn even eat ah meal
Yuh sure it ehn lime all yuh wrappin' in orange peel?

De coconut hah water?

Amryl Johnson
Trinidad/UK

97

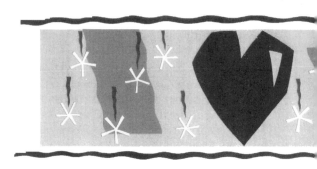

5 Tales Dubs Chants

Brief Encounter

a man waits alone in a subway
with the world in his pocket

he puts his hand in his pocket
the world feels good
firm and round like a breast
he takes it out, kisses it
puts it back again

the world feels good

he keeps his hand on the world
the whole time
stroking it, patting it, keeping it in place

his hands are happy
but his eyes look for enemies

he waits for a woman to pass him in the darkness
'I'll show you the world,' he says
'if you'll come home with me.'

the woman looks at him and smiles
she opens her breast and takes out a heart
perfectly round
the heart turns slowly in the night

a globe

'There is more than one world,' she says
and walks away

Ann Ziety
UK

Beverley's Saga

(For Beverley and Jamaican dub-poet, Jean Binta Breeze)

Me good friend Beverley
Come to England. She was three.
She born in Jamaica, but seh,
Dis ya she country.
She ancestor blood help fe build it,
Dat is history.
Dih black presence go back
Two, three century.

She seh she fadder
Was minding he own business
Back in Jam-country,
Wid he lickle piece-o-land
An he lickle donkey
When dey sen he fe enlist
In de British Army.
Yes, he hads was to fight
Fe dis ya country.
Dey even give he medal fe bravery.

So policeman na come
Wid no brutality.
Mister Repatriation, yuh know,
You will haffi kill she
Cause she na go no whey
Dis ya she country.
Summer is hearts
An she dread de wintry
But she have she lickle flat
An she have she lickle key.

She seh she like it fine
She a pop wid style
You can never put she back inna no woodpile
Or she bun it to de ground.

She seh she went to Uncle Sam
For a six-week vacation,
But after three week
She homesick fe England.
When de plane mek a touch-down
She feel so happy,
She feel she a come home,
Dis ya she country.
If dey think bout repatriation
Dem will haffi kill she.

De odder day
Wan ole English lady stop she,
Seh, 'Miss are you on holiday?'
Bev seh, 'Me not on holiday,
Me a live right hey.
Me na plan fe go no whey.'

De ole lady open she eye, surprisedly,
Bev seh, 'Is Black British dey call we.'
She seh, 'I don't mean to be unkind
But leh me tell you lickle history –
You see all dis big fat architectry?
In it is de blood of my ancestry.
Dih black presence go back
Two, three century.
Don't look at me so bemusedly.'

Bev seh, 'In any case, you been my country first,
So we come back inna kinda reverse.
Isn't life funny? Dis ya. Dis ya history.
O mek we tek a lickle walk,
It so nice an sunny.
Summer is hearts,
An a dread de wintry.
But a have me lickle flat
An a have me lickle key.
You want to come in
For a lickle cup-o-tea?'

Grace Nichols
Guyana/UK

The Women of Mumbles Head

The moon is sixpence,
a pillar of salt or
a shoal of herring.
But on such a night,
wild as the wet wind,
larger than life,
she casts a long line
over the slippery sea.
And the women of Mumbles Head
are one, a long line,
over the slippery sea.
Wet clothes clog them,
heavy ropes tire them,
but the women of Mumbles Head
are one, a long line,
over the slippery sea.
And under white beams
their strong arms glisten,
like silver, like salt,
like a shoal of herring,
under the slippery sea.
And they haul
for their dear ones,
and they call
for their dear ones,
casting a long line
over the slippery sea.
But the mounting waves
draw from them,
the mountain waves
draw from them,
the bodies of their dear ones,
O, the bodies of their dear ones,
drawn under the slippery sea.

In a chain of shawls
they hook one in,
fish-wet, moonlit,
they've plucked him back
from under the slippery sea.
For the moon is sixpence,
a pillar of salt
or a shoal of herring,
and the women of Mumbles Head
are one, a long line
over the slippery sea.

Maura Dooley
UK

Where the Scattering Began

Here
where the scattering began
they come to find their faces
again
to measure the rhythm of their paces
against the call of the drum
that talks
against the wail of the piano
that yields music to the thumbs
they come with faces denying their
names gone English
Irish
Scottish
they come with hands that speak
in ways the tongue has forgotten
they come with eyes that tell a story
the brain cannot recall
they come with the blue of the sea so close
that they lift their eyes with yearning
towards the emptiness of the skies
some come with the memory of forest sounds
that they have never known
they come speaking simply of complicated things

Here
hands and eyes and ears
begin to shape answers
to questions
tongue can find no words
for asking

Merle Collins
Grenada/UK

Problems with Hurricanes

A campesino looked at the air
And told me:
With hurricanes it's not the wind
or the noise or the water.
I'll tell you he said:
it's the mangoes, avocados
Green plantains and bananas
flying into town like projectiles.

How would your family
feel if they had to tell
The generations that you
got killed by a flying
Banana.

Death by drowning has honor
If the wind picked you up
and slammed you
Against a mountain boulder
This would not carry shame
But
to suffer a mango smashing
Your skull
or a plantain hitting your
Temple at 70 miles per hour
is the ultimate disgrace.

The campesino takes off his hat –
As a sign of respect
towards the fury of the wind
And says:
Don't worry about the noise
Don't worry about the water
Don't worry about the wind –

If you are going out
beware of mangoes
And all such beautiful
sweet things.

Victor Hernandez Cruz
Puerto Rico

The Most Precious Thing
A Jewish folktale

A merchant lived in Sidon long ago
Who had been married for ten years or so,
Quite happily except for one sad thing –
Their silent home was never known to ring
With children's voices. We today might say
That this was not a tragedy, but they
Felt differently in that far time and place:
To have no heir was viewed as dark disgrace.

And so the husband went with heavy heart
To see the Rabbi and arrange to part
From his dear wife. The Rabbi sadly said,
'So be it. But remember, when you wed,
You held a splendid feast? Well, I commend
That you should also celebrate the end
Of your good marriage with another feast.
You owe that to your faithful wife at least.'

Before the feast began the merchant took
His wife aside and said to her, 'Now look,
I feel so guilty treating you this way.
You know I love you more than words can say,
Yet I must have a child. We've not been blessed,
So we must part. But you must choose the best,
Most precious thing in all the house before
You leave, and you may keep it evermore.'

She smiled her thanks. And when the feast began
She saw he drank more wine than anyone,
And very soon both he and darkness fell;
He drowned in sleep's unfathomable well.
When he awoke he did not recognize
The room in which he lay. To his surprise
His wife came in and kissed his puzzled brow
And said she hoped that he felt better now.
'Where am I?' he exclaimed. 'This room? This
    bed?'
'You're in my father's house,' she, smiling, said.
'I told the serving men to bring you here.
You said that I could take the thing most dear
And precious from the house. Well, that was you.
You are the dearest thing to me.' He knew
That moment that he could not part from this
Sweet loving wife, so he returned her kiss.

Then off they went to tell the Rabbi; he
Was glad to hear their news and so all three
Knelt and prayed to God that there would be
A child to make complete the couple's joy;
And in the following spring a healthy boy
Was born to them in answer to that prayer,
And happiness, like birdsong, filled the air
And made a second Eden blossom there.

Vernon Scannell
England

109

The Indian Tree

A learned man once said,
just for the sake of saying *something*,
'There is a tree in India.
If you eat the fruit of that tree,
you'll never grow old, and never die.'

Stories about 'The Tree' were passed around,
and finally a king sent his envoy to India
to look for it. People laughed at the man.
They slapped him on the back and called out,

'Sir, I know where your tree is,
but it's far in the jungle,
and you'll need a ladder!'

He kept travelling, following such directions,
and feeling foolish, for years.

He was about to return to the king,
when he met a wise man.
                          'Great teacher,
show me some kindness in this search
for the tree!'
              'My son, this is not an actual tree,
though sometimes it has been called that.
Sometimes it's called a "sun", and sometimes an
"ocean", or a "cloud".
                        All these words
point to the wisdom which comes through
a True Human Being, which may have many effects,
the least of which is eternal life!

In the same way that one person can be a father
to you and a son to someone else, an uncle
to another, and a nephew to yet another,
so what you are looking for
has many names, and one existence.

110

Don't search for one of the names.
Move beyond any attachment to names!'

Every war, and every conflict between human beings,
has happened because of this disagreement
about *names*. It's such an unnecessary foolishness,
because just beyond the arguing,
there's a long table of companionship, set,
and waiting for us to sit down.

Rumi
Persia 13th century

Ring Song

Once upon a time there was a story
It was not a long story …
It was a short story …
A good story …

It had neither a beginning, a middle
Or an end …

First of all the story was told to a child –
The child smiled and said '*Tell me another*'

And the story was told to a man of influence –
The man of influence ignored it

The story was told to a critic –
The critic stuffed his shirt with it

The story was told to a theologian –
The theologian doubted

The story was told to a soldier –
The soldier tore off its wings
And wore them on his helmet

The story was told to a historian –
'*These are not facts*' said the historian

The story was told to a politician –
The politician also smiled but said nothing

The story was told to a government
Who debated it, amended it –
And, finally, refused to pass it

The story was told to a policeman –
The policeman took out his notebook
The story was told to a judge –

'*What is a story?*' asked the judge

The story was told to the hangman
Who wove it in his rope like hair

The story was told to a man in chains
Who made good his escape in it

The story was told to a juggler
Who threw it in the air and caught it
and threw it in the air and caught it
and threw it in the air …

The story was told to an acrobat
Who suspended it below him

The story was told to a sculptor
Who hammered it into the shape of his mother

The story was told to a painter
Who signed it in the corner
And hung it on the wall

And the story was told to a man of the sea
Who opened the story and sailed out upon it

The story was told to a young girl
Whose mirror it became

The story was told to a bird –
The bird built a nest in its branches

And the story was told to a poet
And the poet passed on the story

And this was the story …

Once upon a time there was a story
It was not a long story …
It was a short story …
A good story …

It had neither a beginning, a middle
Or an end …

Pete Morgan
UK

Snowman Chant

ice flakes
       sifting
       sifting
       sifting
on his head
on his head
        he is dead
        he is dead
oh,
snow,
     oh,
snow,
     oh,
snow,
     man.
       You are a cold son of a bitch
            no sun
              sun
              sun
              sun
                in your face.
Shiver,
     snowman,
I have your sliver
of ice
in my eye.
       It burns.
       Why?
       It burns,
oh,
snowman,
oh,
snowman.
       You are definitely a cold sonofabitch

Diane Wakowski
USA

Chant of a Rock

So long, so long——
Forty thousand years
I wait for you.

At last
After forty thousand years
You come back to me.

These days
They call me a giant monolith of Tierra del Australia.
No, I'm neither rock nor cave.

    Look at my skin, touch my skin!
    Why is it so shiny?
    Ah, black diamond!
    Brighter than the Milky Way.
    Why is it so polished, so refined?

    Me ——
    Tended, caressed, loved
    By your fingers
    By your eyes
    By your heart
    By your songs
    Forty thousand years.

    Look at my skin, touch my skin!
    Shiny——warm——tough.
    Full of light
    Full of strength
    Full of love.

    Touch me tenderly with your fingers
    As your gran'pa did yesterday.

Kiss me softly with your lips
As your gran'ma did last year.

Sleep on me in peace
As you did forty thousand years ago.

Australia——a wonderful dreamland forever.
Now they call me a treasure of Commonwealth of Australia.

Ladies and gentlemen,
Welcome to the dreamland!
Welcome to the magical rock!

Please enter air-conditioned Australia.
Please enjoy air-conditioned Australia.

But, ladies and gentlemen,
Don't forget what happened here in the dreamtime.

Remember Wounded Knee in Australia
Remember Auschwitz in Australia
Remember Hiroshima in Australia
Remember a shiny rock in the dreamland!

So long, so long——
Forty thousand years
I wait for you.

Nanao Sakaki
Japan

Who Killed Davey Moore?

Who killed Davey Moore,
Why an' what's the reason for?

'Not I,' says the referee,
'Don't point your finger at me.
I could've stopped it in the eighth
An' maybe kept him from his fate,
But the crowd would've booed, I'm sure,
At not gettin' their money's worth.
It's too bad he had to go,
But there was a pressure on me too, you know.
It wasn't me that made him fall.
No, you can't blame me at all.'

Who killed Davey Moore,
Why an' what's the reason for?

'Not us,' says the angry crowd,
Whose screams filled the arena loud.
'It's too bad he died that night
But we just like to see a fight.
We didn't mean for him t' meet his death,
We just meant to see some sweat,
There ain't nothing wrong in that.
It wasn't us that made him fall.
No, you can't blame us at all.'

Who killed Davey Moore,
Why an' what's the reason for?

'Not me,' says his manager,
Puffing on a big cigar.
'It's hard to say, it's hard to tell,
I always thought that he was well.
It's too bad for his wife an' kids he's dead,
But if he was sick, he should've said.
It wasn't me that made him fall.
No, you can't blame me at all.'

118

Who killed Davey Moore,
Why an' what's the reason for?

'Not me,' says the gambling man
With his ticket stub still in his hand.
'It wasn't me that knocked him down,
My hands never touched him none.
I didn't commit no ugly sin,
Anyway, I put money on him to win.
It wasn't me that made him fall.
No, you can't blame me at all.'

Who killed Davey Moore,
Why an' what's the reason for?

'Not me,' says the boxing writer,
Pounding print on his old typewriter,
Sayin', 'Boxing ain't to blame,
There's just as much danger in a football game'.
Sayin', 'Fist fighting is here to stay,
It's just the old American way.
It wasn't me that made him fall.
No, you can't blame me at all.'

Who killed Davey Moore,
Why an' what's the reason for?

'Not me,' says the man whose fists
Laid him low in a cloud of mist,
Who came here from Cuba's door
Where boxing ain't allowed no more.
'I hit him, yes, it's true,
But that's what I am paid to do.
Don't say "murder", don't say "kill".
It was destiny, it was God's will.'

Who killed Davey Moore,
Why an' what's the reason for?

Bob Dylan
USA

119

from **The Names of the Hare**

The wimount, the messer,
the skidaddler, the nibbler,
the ill-met, the slabber.

The quick-scut, the dew-flirt,
the grass-biter, the goibert,
the home-late, the do-the-dirt.

The starer, the wood-cat,
the purblind, the furze cat,
the skulker, the bleary-eyed,
the wall-eyed, the glance-aside
and also the hedge-springer.

The stubble-stag, the long lugs,
the stook-deer, the frisky legs,
the wild one, the skipper,
the hug-the-ground, the lurker,
the race-the-wind, the skulker,
the shag-the-hare, the hedge-squatter.

The dew-hammer, the dew-hopper,
the sit-tight, the grass-hopper,
the jig-foot, the earth-sitter,
the light-foot, the fern-sitter,
the kail-stag, the growth-cropper.

The creep-along, the sitter-still,
the pintail, the ring-the-hill,
the sudden start,
the shake-the-heart,
the belly-white,
the lambs-in-flight.

The gobshite, the gum-sucker,
the scare-the-man, the faith-breaker,
the snuff-the-ground, the baldy skull,
(his chief name is scoundrel.)

The stag that sprouts the leathery horn,
the creature living in the corn,
the creature bearing all men's scorn,
the creature no one dares to name.

When you have got all this said
then the hare's strength has been laid.
Then you might go faring forth –
east and west and south and north,
wherever you incline to go –
but only if you're skilful too.
And now, Sir Hare, good-day to you.
God guide you to a how-d'ye-do
with me: come to me dead
in either onion broth or bread.

Seamus Heaney
Ireland

Lady Godiva 1040-1080

Lady Godiva,
Let your hair down!
Bare you must go
Through Coventry Town,
Riding your palfrey
Past window and door
Naked as Eve,
For love of the poor.

Lady Godiva
Pity implored
For the poor people
Oppressed by her lord.
'Pity, my lady!'
He sneered as he spake,
'What would *you* suffer
For pity's sweet sake?'

'Lady Godiva,
Mount your white mare!
Ride along Coventry
Street if you dare
Stripped of your clothes
From your gown to your shift –
Do this, and pity
I'll grant as a gift!'

Lady Godiva
Through Coventry sent
Word that all windows
And doors should be pent;
She stripped off her shift,
And her hair she unbound,
It fell, a gold mantle,
Her body around.

Lady Godiva
Sat fair on her seat;
There wasn't a soul
To be seen in the street,
Or a sound to be heard
By the people inside
Save the clack on the cobbles
That told of her ride.

Lady Godiva
Did none see at all?
A fellow named Tom
Made a hole in his wall;
He peeped as she passed,
All golden and white;
But heaven sent lightning
And stripped him of sight.

Lady Godiva
Rode naked to prove
That shame and injustice
Are weaker than love.
Cloaked in her hair
She rode back as she came;
Her lord kept his word
And her folk blessed her name.

Eleanor & Herbert Farjeon
UK

Traffic Lights

Red light
Stop
Green light
Go
Red light
Green light
Red light
Green light
Stop
Stop
Go
Go
Red light
Red light
Where's the green light
A pregnant woman in a car
Gives birth in a car
The boy grows up
Falls in love
And gets married in a car
Has children
And reads magazines and newspapers
In a car
They round him up
And put him in the boot of a car
They draft him and he dies a martyr
Behind the windscreen of a car
They bury him under the wheels of a car
And the car is still in the street
Waiting for the green light
Red light
Stop
Green light
Go
Red light green light

Mu'in Besseisso
Lebanon

Introduction of the Child to the Cosmos

Ho! Ye Sun, Moon, Stars, all ye that move in the heavens,
    I bid you hear me!
Into your midst has come a new life.
    Consent ye, I implore!
Make its path smooth, that it may reach the brow of the first hill!
Ho! Ye Winds, Clouds, Rain, Mist, all ye that move in the air,
    I bid you hear me!
Ho! Ye Hills, Valleys, Rivers, Lakes, Trees, Grasses, all ye of the earth …
Ho! Ye Birds, great and small, that fly in the air,
Ho! Ye Animals, great and small, that dwell in the forest,
Ho! Ye Insects that creep among the grasses and burrow in the
    ground …
Ho! All ye of the heavens, all ye of the air, all ye of the earth:
I bid you all to hear me!
Into your midst has come a new life.
    Consent ye, consent ye all, I implore!
Make its path smooth – then shall it travel
    Beyond the four hills.

Traditional Omaha Indian

124

Visit to the dentist

What a likkle cry baby!
Look how de bwoy a bawl,
One likkle injection him get,
Him no ha' no shame at all.

Ah bet him older than me, Mama,
But me wouldn' cry so loud,
In fac' me wouldn' cry at all
Especially eena crowd.

An look how people a look pon him,
Me shame fe him yuh see,
Me couldn' show me face again
If that likkle bwoy was me.

Eh eh, but look noh, Mama,
One other one a cry,
An the girl who a come out now
Water full up here yeye.

But feba something really wrong
Else them wouldn' frighten so
Mama, guess what happen,
Me toothache gone, yuh know.

The nurse a call we, Mama,
But a couldn' fe we time a'ready?
'Pickney before big people'
Mek the likkle girl go before me.

She go a'ready? A me one lef?
Nurse, tell the dentist noh fe bother,
Me toothache gone fe good now
Unless him want fe see me mother?

Mama, yuh wouldn' force me
An know how me fraid o' needle too,
No badda carry me een there,
Waia! Smaddy come help me, do!

Waia! Murder! Help! Police!
No mek him touch me, oh!
Me heart not too good, Doctor,
Me will dead from fright yuh know.

Wait, Mama, yuh hear that?
Him cyan do nutten when me gum swell soh,
So me mus tek some aspirin tonight
An come back come see him tomorrow.

This dentist is a nice man,
Him smile so sweet an warm,
What mek them pickney cry-cry soh?
Him wouldn' do them any harm.

Watch that one there still a bawl,
The pickney noh have no shame,
Me woulda never mek so much noise
(Me glad me get 'way today all the same).

Valerie Bloom
Jamaica/UK

Moloney and the Dust

Before Mike Nelligan died, Moloney said,
He willed that he wanted to be cremated
And to have every grain of his mortal dust
Scattered abroad in the Shannon. He asked
Me once, since I was his friend,
If I'd scatter him to the Shannon wind.
I thought for a while 'twas fearful odd
But there's many a way to go to God
And this was as good as any. Nelligan, I said,
I'll be glad to scatter you after you're dead!

    Years later, Mike Nelligan died
An' I arranged to have him cremated.
At death he weighed over sixteen stone
But when the burnin' was done
Nelligan fitted in a small box
That I tucked away in my arse-pocket,
As fine a dust as could blow your way
When the wind plays games of a summer's day.

    Well, I hired a boat at Tarbert Quay
And rowed out into the Shannon
Till I was a fair distance from the land.
Then I stopped, pulled in the oars,
Stood up in the boat and looked around.
Not a sinner in sight except myself
And a mangy seagull overhead.
The day was as good as you'd hope to find
Except for a tricky Shannon wind.

I looked around for another minute,
Then I took Mike Nelligan out o' my pocket.
With a final look at the dust o' the dead
I pitched it high above my head.
It seemed for a moment to stick in the air
As if 'twould linger forever there
But that tricky hoor of a Shannon wind
Blew it straight back into my mouth
And I swear to God before I could tell
What had happened, I could feel
The dust slippin' down my throat
And not a thing could I do about it.
It took me several minutes to see
Exactly what had happened to me.
In the blink of an eye, after all my pains,
I had swallowed Mike Nelligan's mortal remains
Or a large part o' them, anyway.

For a while, as I'm sure you'll understand,
I thought I'd go clean out of my mind.
I'm not the kind to swallow a friend.
But then I thought what I had to think.
I'll go back to Tarbert for a drink
And pray for the peace of Nelligan's soul.
What does it matter after all
Where the dead will come to rest –
In seas no human heart has blessed?
Hacked fields of awful wars?
Mockin' faces of the stars?
Or it may happen that the dead are blown
Back in the guts of a livin' man.
Through fire or water, sane or mad,
There's many a way to go to God.
And why should it matter how a man will go?
That Shannon wind will always blow.

Without further delay, with peace of mind,
I started to row me back to land.
One mangy seagull in the sky
Was all I had for company
Till I stood in a pub in Tarbert town
And washed my good friend Nelligan down.
Mike Nelligan's dust and Arthur Guinness
Mingled happily within me.
'God rest you, Mike,' I said as I drank,
Thinking how fire had made him shrink,
'God rest your dust in river and sea
And God rest the rest of your dust in me.'

Brendan Kennelly
Ireland

The Race to Get to Sleep

They're on their marks, they're set,
They're off!

Matthew's kicking off his shoes!
Penny's struggling out of her jumper!
He's ripping off his trousers!
She's got one sock off! Now the other's off!
But Matthew's still winning! No, he's not!
It's Penny! Penny's in the lead!
She's down to her knickers!
She's racing out of the room!
She's racing upstairs!
Matthew's right behind her!
There's a fight on the landing!
There's a scramble at the bathroom door!
It's Penny! It's Matthew! It's …
Splash!
They're both in the bath!
But there's a hitch!
Matthew's got soap in his eye!
Penny's got soap up her nose!
They're stalling! But no, they're both fine!
They're both out the bath! They're neck and neck!
It's Matthew! It's Penny! It's Matthew!
Now it's Penny again! She's ahead!
She's first on with her pyjamas!
Now Matthew's catching up! There's nothing in it!
They're climbing into their beds!
Matthew's in the lead with one eye closed!
Now it's Penny again! She's got both closed!
So's Matthew! He's catching up!

It's impossible to tell who's winning!
They're both absolutely quiet!
There's not a murmur from either of them.
It's Matthew! It's Penny! It's …
It's a draw! A draw!

But no! Wait a moment! It's not a draw!
Matthew's opened an eye!
He's asking if Penny's asleep yet!
He's disqualified!
So's Penny! She's doing the same!
She's asking if Matthew's asleep yet!
It's impossible! It's daft!
It's the hardest race in the world!

Brian Patten
England

Tell Me, Tell Me, Sarah Jane

Tell me, tell me, Sarah Jane,
    Tell me, dearest daughter,
Why are you holding in your hand
    A thimbleful of water?
Why do you hold it to your eye
    And gaze both late and soon
From early morning light until
    The rising of the moon?

Mother, I hear the mermaids cry,
    I hear the mermen sing,
And I can see the sailing-ships
    All made of sticks and string.
And I can see the jumping fish,
    The whales that fall and rise
And swim about the waterspout
    That swarms up to the skies.

Tell me, tell me, Sarah Jane,
    Tell your darling mother,
Why do you walk beside the tide
    As though you loved none other?
Why do you listen to a shell
    And watch the billows curl,
And throw away your diamond ring
    And wear instead the pearl?

Mother I hear the water
    Beneath the headland pinned,
And I can see the sea-gull
    Sliding down the wind.
I taste the salt upon my tongue
    As sweet as sweet can be.

Tell me, my dear, whose voice you hear?

It is the sea, the sea.

Charles Causley
England

132

A Nursery Rhyme

This little digit went to market,
This little digit stayed home.
That little digit went with this little digit.
This little digit did the same.

This little digit made an error.
That little digit made none.
This little digit went wrong wrong wrong
All the way home.

This little digit had no place in the file.
That little digit had the key.
This little digit went from file to file:
'Is there no place for me?'

This little digit was put in the store.
That little digit was not.
This big store knew more and more
For every digit it got.

This little switch went on-off-on.
That little switch went pop.
So all the digits were sent one way
Stop stop stop stop stop.

Call the mechanic to mend the switch:
Hark how the circuits stutter.
This little digit went this little digit
Went this little - ah, that's better.

Laurence Lerner
UK

6 Drumwork Bodywork

When I Dance

When I dance it isn't merely
That music absorbs my shyness,
My laughter settles in my eyes,
My swings of arms convert my frills
As timing tunes my feet with floor
As if I never just looked on.

It is that when I dance
O music expands my hearing
And it wants no mathematics
It wants no thinking, no speaking,
It only wants all my feeling
In with animation of place.

When I dance it isn't merely
That surprises dictate my movements,
Other rhythms move my rhythms,
I uncradle rocking-memory
And skipping, hopping and running
All mix movements I balance in.

It is that when I dance
I'm costumed in a rainbow mood,
I'm okay at any angle,
Outfit of drums crowds madness round,
Talking winds and plucked strings conspire,
Beat after beat warms me like sun.

When I dance it isn't merely
I shift bodyweight balances
As movement amasses my show,
I celebrate each dancer here,
No sleep invades me now at all
And I see how I am tireless.

It is that when I dance
I gather up all my senses
Well into hearing and feeling,
With body's flexible postures
Telling their poetry in movement
And I celebrate all rhythms.

James Berry
Jamaica/UK

Current Notes

Sing me a song of sixpence
now that the dollar is ready to die

Play a tune for all the food
my salary used to buy

Well how about a ragtime band
for beggars stretching out the hand

Maybe a touch of disco rock
for the madman facing electric shock

Say, play me some Coltrane blues
for children walking without shoes

or dub some heavy drum and bass
for a sister with a swollen waist

a note
a chord
a bar
a rest
could easily end the strain

Jean Binta Breeze,
Jamaica

Jab Jab

Out of masquerading crowds
they come shuffle-dancing.
Jester-clowns in brilliant satin,
armoured against the lashing whip:
stuffed up like bobolee.
Black face in white face wire mask.
Arms circle in air, whips flash,
crack like gunshots:

We are the boys, jab jab,
from Fyzabad, jab jab,
we fraid nobody, jab jab,
we big and bad, jab jab,
lookin fuh trouble, jab jab,
in Port-of-Spain, jab jab,
we ready and able, jab jab,
so think again, jab jab,
if yuh want to fight, jab jab,
you have no chance, jab jab,
against our might, jab jab,
so shift yuh stance, jab jab,
find yuh money, jab jab,
prepare to pay, jab jab,
or everybody, jab, jab,
will rue de day, jab jab,
an only den, jab jab,
I'll go away, jab jab
jingle jingle, jab jab,
jingle jingle, jab jab,
jingle jingle, jab jab.

John Lyons
Trinidad/UK

Jaywalkin'

I like to sleep all day and play around all night
I always cross the street against the traffic-light
I'm always ready to upset the status quo
When it says green I stop. When it says red I go

Jaywalkin', travellin' against the lights
Jaywalkin', mixin' up days and nights

I'm always getting hooked on someone else's high
I'm always getting caught without an alibi
If you're in love with me don't ever let it show
When it says green I stop, when it says red I go

Jaywalkin', breakin' all the rules
Jaywalkin', takin' the road for fools

Won't ever do a thing because it's good for me
I got to be bad to show myself I'm free
If it's a witch's brew just watch me drain the cup
I guess the answer is I'm scared of growing up

Jaywalkin', goin' on crazy flights
Jaywalkin', travellin' against the lights
Jaywalkin'

Fran Landesman
USA

140

Tap-Dancing
for Liberty Blake

Antics in the attics,
Antics in the cellars,
Upstairs and downstairs,
Tap-dancing fellahs!

Bill Bojangles, Buck and Bubbles,
Tap your way through all your troubles!
Bunny and Sandman, Chuckles and Chuck,
Dance your way through all kinds of luck!

Tap your toes and tap your heels,
Let us know how the tapdancer feels!
Tiptop in the morning, toptoe at night,
Tap toes and heels till we all come out right!

Tap to your funeral, tap into the ground,
Tap up to heaven and look around!
Tap Saint Peter and his bunch of keys,
Tap Old Gabriel if you please!
Tap toe and heel every cloud-capped tower
Tap every cloud till it runs a shower!
Tap the old sun for solar power
Tap it to the earth, open every flower!
Tap in the thunder and tap in the rain
Tap till the whole world rings again!

One two, three four five
Tap again till you feel alive!
Six, seven, eight nine ten,
Tap for all you're worth, then tap again!
 Seven, eight, nine ten eleven,
Tap for the earth and tap for heaven!

Geoffrey Summerfield
UK

Bodhrán

I shall take the drum
with both my hands
and beat a madness around

a roaring, a sound
of thunder
rolled in my palms

rocking between my arms
a live heart
rich with the thump of blood.

I shall bend the wood
of a sapling, the skin of a goat
pulled hard and tight

and take it out every night
for the moon
to shape it and shrink it.

Think of it
as my madness
the drumming of rage

or my coming of age
savage joy
beating flesh with a bone

for I've always known
it would happen
I've known it would come

the time of the drum.

It's pounding seas
it's a swarm of bees
it's a storm of rain
it's a dish of grain
it's a womb of blood
it's a tomb of mud
it's a leather shield
it's a sown field

a bear's strength
an owl's stealth
an arm's length
from my deep self

it's the shaman in me
shaman in me
step to my tune
and you'll see.

Hilary Llwellyn-Williams
Wales

Ping-Pong

Swatted between bats
The celluloid ball
Leaps on unseen elastic
Skimming the taut net

Sliced
Screwed
Dabbed

Spun
Cut
Smashed

Point
Service

Ping
Pong
Bing
Bong

Pong
Ping
Bong
Bing

Point
Service

Ding
Dong
Ting
Tang

Dong
Ding
Tong
Tong

Point
Service

Angled
Cut
Floated
Driven

Slipped
Driven
Caressed
Hammered

THWACKED
Point
Service

Bit	Bat
Tip	Tap
Slip	Slap
Zip	Zap
Whip	Whap

Point
Service

Left	Yes
Right	Yes
Twist	Yes
Skids	Yes
Eighteen	Seventeen
Eighteen	All
Nineteen	Eighteen
Nineteen	All
Twenty	Nineteen

Point
Service

Forehand	Backhand
Swerves	Yes
Rockets	Yes
Battered	Ah
Cracked	Ah

SMASHED

SMASHED

SMASHED

GAME

Gareth Owen

If Love Was Jazz

If love was jazz,
I'd be dazzled
By its razzmatazz.

If love was a sax
I'd melt in its brassy flame
Like wax.

If love was a guitar,
I'd pluck its six strings,
Eight to the bar.

If love was a trombone,
I'd feel its slow
Slide, right down my backbone.

If love was a drum,
I'd be caught in its snare,
Kept under its thumb.

If love was a trumpet,
I'd blow it.

If love was jazz,
I'd sing its praises,
Like Larkin has.

But love isn't jazz.
It's an organ recital.
Eminently worthy,
Not nearly as vital.

If love was jazz,
I'd always want more.
I'd be a regular
On that smoky dance-floor.

Linda France
UK

146

Reggae Sounds

Shock-black bubble-doun-beat bouncing
rock-wise tumble-doun soun music
foot-drop find drum bloody story
bass history is a moving
                    is a hurting black story

Thunda from a bass drum sounding
lightning from a trumpet and a organ
bass and rhythm and trumpet double-up
team-up with drums for a deep doun searching

Rhythm of a tropical electric storm
(cooled doun to the pace of the struggle)
flame-rhythm of historically yearning
flame-rhythm of the time of turning
measuring the time for bombs and for burning

Slow drop. make stop. move forward.
dig doun to the root of the pain
shape it into violence for the people
they will know what to do they will do it

Shock-black bubble-doun-beat bouncing
rock-wise tumble-doun soun music
foot-drop find drum bloody story
bass history is a moving
                    is a hurting black story

Linton Kwesi Johnson
Jamaica/UK

Country Dancing

Polka
do it
clap a lot
Polka
do it again
those on the edge do it
posh ones do it
arch, sway their legs, swing
others falter
don't do it, won't do it,
can't do it again.
The caller has rubber lips and stiff arms, he goes:
bop she doobie oobie dub dub rapidly rapidly
pairs walled by tight shoes get their roots pulled;
strip the willow down
move all the chairs into the centre
girls turn round, link up with knotted handkercheifs
    and pass their legs over the men's shoulders
rhythm increases
friends hold each other just in case
backs bent, they make V signs,
most of the men have on flared trousers.
The last part of the dance must be done
speedily because there is very little
time in the music
keep your teeth together
hum, snap your fingers, hum.

Peter Finch
Wales

Worker's Song

Big ships shudder
down to the sea
        because of me
Railroads run
on a twinness track
        'cause of my back
        Whoppa, Whoppa
        Whoppa, Whoppa

Cars stretch to a
super length
        'cause of my strength
Planes fly high
over seas and lands
        'cause of my hands
        Whoppa, Whoppa
        Whoppa, Whoppa

I wake
start the factory humming
I work late
keep the whole world running
and I got something … something
coming … coming …
        Whoppa
        Whoppa
        Whoppa

Maya Angelou
African-American

149

The digging song

In your hands you hold the spade,
Feel its well-worn wood,
Now you drive it in the earth,
Drive it deep and good.

> Dig dig digging dirt,
>   Dirt inside your vest.
> Dig dig digging dirt.
>   Digging dirt is best.

Here are worms that twist and loop
Tight as knots in string,
Here are spiders, ants and bugs
Running in a ring.

> Dig dig digging dirt,
>   Dirt inside your vest.
> Dig dig digging dirt.
>   Digging dirt is best.

Soon your hands are red and raw,
Blisters on the way,
But your spade just wants to dig
All day all day all day.

> Dig dig digging dirt,
>   Dirt inside your vest.
> Dig dig digging dirt,
>   Digging dirt is best.

Wes Magee
England

Bodywork

Fibula, tibia, tarsals and rib,
clavical, cranium, spine;
whatever the outside appearance,
all praise to the inner design!

I've a mandible, patella, metatarsal,
I have biceps, I have triceps and a brain;
a pulmonary artery takes blood one way,
then back it comes through pulmonary vein.
There's retina and anvil, epiglottis,
oesophagus and pancreas and tongue;
how could I cope without my parathyroids,
Eustachian tube or diaphragm or lung?

Fibula, tibia, tarsals and rib,
clavical, cranium, spine;
whatever I seem from the outside,
you can't fault the inner design!

Judith Nicholls
England

For Ma

Roll roti! roll roti! roll roti! roll roti!
Curry cookin in de karahee
Bora boilin wid de bagee
Woodsmoke sweet in me nose like agarbattee –
Ayuh wake up wake up ayuh pickni wake up ayuh man
Wid de sunshine in yu eye an de river a flow
An brung doves burstin from de trees an de kiskidees
An de whole savannah swimmin green an a glow!

Wata foh fetch battam-house foh daub fresh bucket foh
    mend clothes foh beat
Wake up ayuh pickni wuk na dun wuk foh duh
Cutlass foh shaap wood foh chap fence foh build dat bull
    bruk dung
Is wha da maan a stretch e haan an yaan foh!
Hear a cow baal in de yaad how dem swell wid milk-fraff
Goat a groan dem want go graze an sheep a caff-caff –
Ayuh wake up wake up time na deh foh cry time na deh
    foh laff
Hen a lay an cow a drap time na deh foh stap!

Roll roti! roll roti! roll roti! roll roti!
Curry cooking in the karahie
Bora boiling with the bagee
Woodsmoke sweet in my nose like incense –
Wake up, wake up the lot of you,wake up you children,
	wake up you man
With the sunshine in your eyes and the river flowing
And brown doves bursting from the trees, and the kiskadees
And the whole savannah swimming green and glowing!

Water to fetch, bottom-house to daub afresh, bucket to mend,
	clothes to beat
Wake up you children, work's not done, work's to do
Cutlass to sharpen, wood to chop, fence to rebuild that the bull
	broke down
What's that man stretching his hand and yawning for!
Hear how the cows bawl in the yard, they're swollen with milk
The goats groan, they want to graze, and sheep keep coughing
Wake up you lot, wake up, there's no time to cry, there's no time
	to laugh
Hens are laying, cows are bearing, there's no time to stop!

David Dabydeen
Guyana/UK

Rhythm

Rhythm rhythm
Can you
Hear the
Rhythm

If you listen close
Ears to the ground
The base of noise
Is rhythm's sound
From spoken words
To ways of walk
From rapping to reggae
And funk we talk in

Rhythm rhythm
Can you
Hear the
Rhythm

Way back in the heart of Africa
They took our drums away
But rhythm proved its own power
By being here today

All four corners
Sweet sounding Rhythms reach
With treble in the speakers
And bass in the speech
From the depths of cold
To heat in heights
Mohammid Ali did do it in fights

With
Quick Rhythms
Slick Rhythms
Bold Rhythms
Gold Rhythms
God Given
Rhythm Rhythm
Can you
hear the
Rhythm Rhythm

Rhythm Rhythm
Can you
hear the
Rhythm

Lemn Sissay
Somalia/UK

Father William

'You are old, Father William,' the young man said,
    'And your hair has become very white;
And yet you incessantly stand on your head –
    Do you think, at your age, it is right?'

'In my youth,' Father William replied to his son,
    'I feared it might injure the brain;
But now that I'm perfectly sure I have none,
    Why, I do it again and again.'

'You are old,' said the youth, 'as I mentioned before,
    And have grown most uncommonly fat;
Yet you turned a back somersault in at the door –
    Pray, what is the reason of that?'

'In my youth,' said the sage, as he shook his gray locks,
    'I kept all my limbs very supple
By the use of this ointment – one shilling the box –
    Allow me to sell you a couple.'

'You are old,' said the youth, 'and your jaws are too weak
    For anything tougher than suet;
Yet you finished the goose, with the bones and the beak –
    Pray, how did you manage to do it?'

'In my youth,' said his father, 'I took to the law,
    And argued each case with my wife;
And the muscular strength, which it gave to my jaw,
    Has lasted the rest of my life.'

'You are old,' said the youth, 'one would hardly suppose
    That your eye was as steady as ever;
Yet you balanced an eel on the end of your nose –
    What made you so awfully clever?'

'I have answered three questions, and that is enough,'
    Said his father, 'don't give yourself airs!
Do you think I can listen all day to such stuff?
    Be off, or I'll kick you down stairs.'

Lewis Carroll
England 19th century

from **She Who**

She Who

She, she SHE, she SHE, she WHO?

she – she WHO she – WHO she WHO – SHE?

She, she, who? she WHO? she, WHO SHE?

who who SHE, she – who, she WHO – WHO?

she WHO – who, WHO – who, WHO – who, WHO – who...

She. who – WHO, she WHO. She WHO – who SHE?

who she SHE, who SHE she, SHE – who WHO –

She WHO?

She SHE who, She, she SHE

she SHE, she SHE who.

SHEEE   WHOOOOOO

....

She Who bears it
bear down, breathe
bear down, bear down, breathe
bear down, bear down, bear down, breathe

She Who lies down in the darkness and bears it
She Who lies down in the lightness and bears it
the labor of the She Who carries and bears is the first labor

all over the world
the waters are breaking everywhere
everywhere the waters are breaking
the labor of She Who carries and bears
and raises and rears is the first labor,
there is no other first labor.

Judy Gahn
USA

Working with Poems in my Earphone

In performance

The poems in this collection cry out to be read aloud, to be performed in one way or another to an eager audience. The chance to do so should not be missed:

> *Lend the poem your breath and the poem*
> *will lend you its voice.*

How can you make a poem dance off the page for your listeners? On this and the next page are a few general tips to start you off.

You may want to go through these on your own, or in pairs or in a small group. Two or more heads are often better than one!

- Read the poem through a couple of times quietly to yourself.

- Read it a third or fourth time – aloud – thinking about any special lines or words that catch your eye and ear.

- Now, in preparing to perform the poem, think about:

  - Who is speaking the words of the poem, telling the tale/chanting the chant?

  - Is there one voice – or more than one?

  - Does the poem lend itself to being divided up in any way, perhaps for a group reading?

  - What is the pace of the poem? What is its mood?

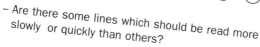

– Are there some lines which should be read more slowly or quickly than others?

– Where should you pause?

– Where are the poem's climaxes?

– Are there any key punchlines?

– How does the poet's punctuation guide you?

– How should your reading best capture the rhyme, the rhythm and the images of the poem?

– What 'body language' do you need to help the works along?

– Would it be good to add sound effects or have other props for performance?

☑ Rehearse.

☑ Learn your lines.

☑ Deliver!

☑ Record on cassette/video.

☑ Review your performance.

And remember:

Words dancin
words dancin
till dey sweat
words like fishes
jumpin out a net
words wild and free
joinin de poetry revelry
words back to back
words belly to belly

161

The following performance ideas are linked to particular poems. You can of course adapt and extend them to any of the poems in this collection and to other poems you know and enjoy.

1 Lend the Poem Your Breath

1 Poetry Jump-Up   Web of Sound

Find some accompanying calypso music – either recorded or live instruments – and stage a carnival reading. Think carefully about how you mix music and words so that you can hear both clearly. Experiment with beat and volume.

2 Belongings with a Beat

1 Track Suit   MY BAG   Spell to Summon the Owner of the Shoes   Leaflets

Plan a performance of these poems using colourful props. How will you show off your track suit and bag? Gather together leaflets from different sources to give out to your audience as you perform. Demonstrate the magic of the shoes.

2 Madam   The Car   Ladders

The challenge with these three poems is how to make repetition interesting to your audience. Try different accents, a varied pace, a few well-timed pauses. Look for phrases that will intrigue your listeners such as 'The car I picked peaches for' and 'Ladders for lofts with ghosts inside'.

3 Money moans

One person reads the word 'money'. Another reads the rest. Change your pace, your tone of voice, your mood, your facial expressions as you perform. Think about the final three lines – how do you want to leave your audience feeling?

4 Zoe's Ear-rings   If I Had a Hundred Hats
  A Peach Dress   The Glassy Green and Maroon

Think yourself into fashion-show mood. Read these four poems as part of the fashion parade on the boardwalk. What music do you need? Colourful props would make your performance sing!

5 A Child's Christmas in Cardiff   Computer Game

Decide how you will handle CAPITAL LETTERS and exclamations! Enjoy all those onomatopoeic words: ZAP! POW! BAM! Hit your audience between the eyes and ears – but don't overdo it. . .

6 Night Mail

Recall the sounds and rhythm on the rails of a train – particularly a steam engine. What's the poem's pace? Where does it slow down and speed up? Some wonderful words to get your voice-box around.

3 Raps Boasts Rants

1 Bawd   I am a girl who loves to shoot   The Complete Alternative History of the World, Part One

Here the female voice boasts. Which are the key words to stress? How will you pose on stage? What looks will you give your audience? With your body language make them feel *you* are in charge!

2 Rogan the Lion's Roaring Song

A poem that you should have fun with in a group performance. Invite your audience to join in at key points – you'll need to warm them up. Like Roald Dahl's animals, this lion has some nice and some nasty habits; make sure you contrast them clearly in performance.

163

3 The Michael Rosen Rap   Baby-K Rap Rhyme
  Overstanding   The Blank Generation

Listen to some rap music on tape. Now perform your own rap
versions of these poems. Practise the rhythm. Which words / phrases
need a special click of the fingers? What special treatment can you
give to the choruses?

4 O, that I were the son of Andriamanitra!   The Mystery
  The Boast of the Good Farmer   Party Man

The narrators of these poems are very different. Who are they?
How are they thinking and feeling? Climb inside their skins as you
prepare to perform. Convey their separate mysteries to your audience.

5 Prayer Before Birth   Masters of War

Listen to a recording of the song 'Masters of War' by Bob Dylan.
What do these two poems have in common? Put across their power
and depth of feeling in your readings. Exploit their closing lines to get
audience reaction.

4 Monologues Dialogues Dialtones

1 The party to which you were not invited   Parrot

An important question here – are these best read by one or two voices?
They are the sort of poems that you could expand quite easily. Try
improvising some extra lines for either poem, keeping the same style.

2 New Baby   My Dad   Mum Takes a Bath

Three poems to be performed under the title of 'Family Life'.
Search for all the deep-felt emotions and domestic detail.
What looks do they give each other?

3 Don't ask me   Boy   About Friends   Message

These four are monologues, poems for a single voice. What should be the tone of the readings? Can you capture their inner feelings?

4 Small-town Sunday   Leaves   Who's There?

These are conversations. Reflect on the ideas the poets are exploring. Make the questions in each poem clear to your audience. You'll need to plan readings carefully so that the various voices are distinctive and flow on smoothly from one another.

5 Phone Booth   What Is This in Reference To?

Telephones and dial-tones: loved by poets, ideal props for performance poetry. Look for the key words. Get the pace – and the pauses – of the poems just right.

6 Weather Rapport

The challenge here is to put across to your listeners the play on words:
    weather / whether
    report / rapport
How can you best do that? Would two speakers – with flash cards! – work? Make sure you capture the rhythm and the rap.

7 Market Women's Cries   Granny in de Market Place

The first poem was written about 300 years ago; the second ten years ago; their setting and subject matter are timeless. Appeal to the five senses in your performance: touch, taste, sight, smell, sound. Bring out the humour.

5 Tales Dubs Chants

1 Brief Encounter   The Most Precious Thing

Two moving tales. Think hard about their pace and mood. Which words will your reading dwell upon? How will you interpret the male and female voices?

2 The Women of Mumbles Head Where the Scattering Began

Here the atmosphere and the ideas behind the works are important. In the first poem you want your audience to *see* and *feel* the wild wet night. In the second, make them reflect on the title – and you'll need to decide where the pauses come because there's no punctuation to guide you.

3 Beverley's Saga   Visit to the dentist

The Caribbean pulse lies deep in these stories. Work out the rhythms and the rhyme you want to convey. How will you handle the dialogue? Capture the playful tone and emotions of the female narrators.

4 Snowman Chant   Chant of a Rock   *from* The Names of the Hare

Three very different chants to test your rhythmic powers. Study first how the poets have set out their verse – that will help you with breathing, pace and pauses. Vary the volume. Relish the tongue-twisters.

5 Who Killed Davey Moore?

Plan a group reading of this poem. The refrain of:

> *Who killed Davey Moore,*
> *Why an' what's the reason for?*

needs a distinctive voice. This was originally written as a protest song, so think about possible musical accompaniment. Lots of strong emotions should come out in performance.

6 Moloney and the Dust

A delicious tale. Set your scene, build up the humour and tension –
whatever will happen next? Seize those punch lines:

In the blink of an eye, after all my pains,
I had swallowed Mike Nelligan's mortal remains

Be sure you end on a note of hushed reverence. . .

7 A Nursery Rhyme

A nursery rhyme for the computer age: try performing this poem in a
group, using 'computer voices'. Inventive body language and sound
effects go well with the verses. Think about the last lines – what's
happening? Make your audience *think*.

6 Drumwork Bodywork

1 When I Dance   Tap-Dancing   Country Dancing

These three need to be set to dance steps of your own design.
Rehearse in groups – relax yourself, dance away. Mirror the words and
the steps. Perhaps three of you could perform the words, and three do
the dancing.

2 Jab Jab   Jaywalkin'   Ping-Pong   Bodywork

Four more active poems – not dance this time but rhythmic gestures.
Match the words to your movements. Practise the difficult words in
'Bodywork' – can you make them sound poetic? In this performance
body language should do some of the talking.

3 Bodhrán   If Love Was Jazz   Reggae Sounds

Think first about the musical backgrounds which these poems are
celebrating. Listen to some Celtic drumming, some jazz and reggae.
Now try to perform these with live music accompaniment. Capture
their very different musical styles and rhythms.

4 Worker's Song   The digging song

Two poems that work well together in performance. Another chance for audience participation in the choruses – words and actions. Would singing work? Try adding another verse to each poem, writing in the same style.

5 Father William

The Lewis Carroll classic – a chance to perform a zany dialogue. Have fun with the body language. Can you make sense of the nonsense? The rhythm and the rhymes are clever.

6 *from* She Who

The birth of a child, the breaking of the waters is a unique and powerful moment in nature – and in any culture. Here's a chance to bury yourself in delicious sounds. As a group, repeat 'She Who' at different volume, different pace.

Use pauses. . .whisper. . . evoke / invoke / provoke.

Language, form and style

1   *Once upon a time there lived*
        a small joke
        in the middle of nowhere
                            page 7

'The magic cloak of fable or parable' – choose five poems in the collection which draw on the power of fable or parable. Discuss and study common features of language and subject matter.

2 Look at how poets use different narrative voices:

- Choose four poems which are told using the first-person 'I' narrator, e.g. 'When I Dance'.
  What are the advantages of this for the poet?

- Now select four poems which employ a third-person narrator, e.g. 'Zoe's Ear-rings'.
  Does this lead to a different kind of poem?

- Do certain subjects lend themselves more easily to either a first or third-person narrative? Do poets tend to favour the 'I' style?

3 Compare any four poems in which the poets use free or unrhymed verse, e.g. 'The party to which you were not invited'. Do you enjoy poetry in this style? Why? What do you find attractive about it?

4 Now look at a group of poems which are set out on the page in an unconventional way, e.g. 'Web of Sound' or 'Ping-Pong'. Analyse why the poet has presented his / her words in such a format.

5 Study four poems which have rhyming verse, e.g. 'Night Mail'. Comment on the poets' choice of vocabulary to achieve the rhymes. Do the rhymes ever seem forced?

Does poetry have to rhyme? Discuss this question in groups, drawing on examples from the collection.

6 Look for some poems which use dialogue between characters. How do the poets manage conversations within a poem? What do you notice about their use of speech marks? Do the conversations make for enjoyable poetry?

7 Re-read a couple of poems which tell unlikely stories, e.g. 'Wife Who Smashed Television Gets Jail' or 'Moloney and the Dust'.

What makes them poetry rather than short stories? Would they be more effective as short stories?

8 Choose three poems which employ a question and answer style, e.g. 'Leaves' or 'Who's There?'

Study how the poets construct these poems. Can you detect similarities in the way they shape sentences and rhymes? Do you enjoy reading them?

9 Look at some poems which use different styles of punctuation, e.g. 'Weather Rapport':

> We don't know WHETHER
> the sun will shine
> we don't know WHETHER
> there'll be a hurricane
> we don't know WHETHER
> we'll get sleet or snow
> we don't know WHETHER
> there'll be a shower of rain. . .
>
> page 90

Also look at 'MY BAG', 'Madam' and 'Brief Encounter'. Analyse why the poets in each case chose the punctuation used. Do you find it confusing or helpful as a reader and performer?

10 The chorus is a popular poetic feature. Look through the collection to find some examples, e.g. 'The digging song'. How does the chorus add to a poem? What is its purpose?

11 Re-read a group of poems which have a distinctive dialect. Study the phrasing carefully and note the features of language which are different from Standard English. How do the poets exploit the dialect? Do you enjoy the poems?

12 Most of the poems in this book were written quite recently by poets who currently perform their work in clubs, at concerts, poetry festivals and in schools and colleges. There are a small number which were written at least fifty years ago and in some cases in previous centuries. Make a list of these. Research their date of composition. Comment on their subject matter, style and use of language. How do they contrast with the modern poetry in this collection?

Further assignments

☐1☐ *Audience participation is an integral part of oral culture whether we think of story-telling, worksongs, or the liturgy of the church with the priest chanting and the congregation answering back.*

page 5

Plan some further performances of any of the poems in the collection in which you involve your audience directly. They will need to be given their words and have a chance to practise.

☐2☐ Choose one or two of the poems which you think might lend themselves to adaptation into a short story or playscript. Why have you chosen the poems that you have? Discuss your reasons in a small group.

Now write your own story or short play using the poet's basic ideas.

☐3☐ Choose three or four poems across the collection that seem to you to have an interesting connection. The connection could be:

- thematic
- stylistic
- cultural
- a similarity of voice
- a similarity of mood

Write about the connections between the poems, exploring the differences as well as the similarities.

☐4☐ Make a chart of themes dealt with in the collection. This could be done as a wall display for the classroom. List the poems around the heading of each theme:

BELONGINGS WITH A BEAT

MONOLOGUES DIALOGUES DIALTONES

DRUMWORK BODYWORK

RAPS BOASTS RANTS

TALES DUBS CHANTS

5 What have been your favourite lines and verses from this collection? Make another wall display in which you write up your favourite quotations from the poems. Add illustrations and photographs which capture the spirit of the poems.

6 Try to look at the anthology *Poems on the Underground* (Cassell), which collects together poems that have appeared on posters in the London Underground stations and trains.

Choose five poems from *Poems in My Earphone* which you think would make for interesting and accessible reading by Underground train travellers. Design an eye-catching poster for each of the poems you have selected. Display along your school/college corridors!

7 Look back over the collection with an eye to those poems written by women and those by men. Do you notice any particular differences in content or style?

Write a commentary on this aspect of *Poems in My Earphone*.

8 Search back through the book and look at the places of origin of each of the writers. Does their poetry appear to be influenced by where they come from? Discuss any trends you detect.

Write up your findings as a magazine feature, in word-processed format if possible.

9 Choose two poems from any of the sections – one you liked and one you didn't enjoy. Write a letter to each of the poets explaining in detail the reasons for your response. Refer closely to the poems themselves, quoting where appropriate.

10 Imagine you have been asked by John Agard to add two more poems to each of the book's sections. Obviously they must suit the title of each section.

Research in the library and in other poetry books you can find and make your selection. Type them up and bind them together in leaflet format, perhaps for inclusion in the class/school library.

11 Write some poems of your own that could fit into any of the sections in *Poems in My Earphone*. Remember that this is a collection of 'performance poetry' where sounds matter!

Some ideas to get you started:

• a 'belongings' poem, in the style of 'Track Suit', 'Money moans' or 'Madam';

• a rhyme, in the style of 'Night Mail';

• free verse, in the style of 'I am a purse...';

• a 'boast' like 'Bawd' or 'The First';

• raps like 'Baby-K Rap Rhyme' and 'Machoman';

• protest verses, in the mould of 'Masters of War';

• conversation pieces, in the style of 'Small-town Sunday';

• a telephone conversation, shaped like 'Phone Booth';

• question-and-answer verses like 'Leaves';

• a circular story, in the style of 'Ring Song';

• shape poems – see 'Snowman Chant';

• narrative verse – see 'Moloney and the Dust';

• poems about dance and body language – see 'Tap Dancing' and 'Ping-Pong'.

NOTE

Many of the poets featured in *Poems in My Earphone* are available to perform their poetry in schools.

For further information, contact your local Writers-in-Schools scheme.

P.S.
'I is a poem today
I mean to have a good time'

Index of poets

Index of first lines

177

ACKNOWLEDGEMENTS

We are grateful to the following copyright holders for permission to reproduce poems:

John Agard c/o Caroline Sheldon Literary Agency for 'Poetry Jump-Up' from *You'll Love This Stuff* (Cambridge University Press, 1986), 'The howdooyoodo' from *New Angles* (Oxford University Press, 1987), 'Prayer to Laughter', 'Once Upon A Time' and 'Laughter's Chant' from *Laughter is an Egg* (Viking, 1990), 'Web of Sound' from *Man to Pan* (Casa de las Americas, 1982); Anvil Press Poetry Ltd for 'Boy' from *The Other Country* by Carol Ann Duffy (1990); Associated University Presses for 'O, that I were the son of Andriamanitra!' from *Haiteny*; Black Sparrow Press for 'Chair Affair' Copyright © 1993 by Wanda Coleman from *Hand Dance* and 'Snowman Chant' Copyright © 1973 by Diane Wakoski from *Dancing on the Grave of a Son of a Bitch*; The Blackstaff Press and Harvill Collins for 'Wife Who Smashed Television Gets Jail' by Paul Durcan from *A Snail in my Prime: New and Selected Poems* (1993) and 'A Peach Dress' by Maighréad Meebh; Bloodaxe Books Ltd for 'The Blank Generation' from *Scornflakes* by Attila The Stockbroker (1992), 'Party Man' from *Watermelon Man* by Katie Donovan (1993), 'The Women of Mumbles Head' from *Explaining Magnetism* by Maura Dooley (1991), 'If Love Was Jazz' from *Red* by Linda France (1992), 'The party to which you were not invited' from *Nude Modelling for the Afterlife* by Henry Normal (1993); Marion Boyars Publishers Ltd for 'MY BAG' from *A Black Pow-Wow of Jazz Poems* by Ted Joans; the author, Jean Binta Breeze for 'Current Notes' from *Riddym Ravings and Other Poems*; Cambridge University Press and the author Valerie Bloom for 'Visit to the dentist' from *Duppy Jamboree*; Carcanet Press Ltd for 'The Glassy Green and Maroon' by Sujata Bhatt from *Monkey Shadows*; the author's agent on behalf of the Estate of Charles Causley for 'Give me a House' from *Jack the Treacle Eater* (Macmillan) and 'Tell Me, Tell Me, Sarah Jane' from *The Poems* (Macmillan, 1992); Coffee House Press for 'Problems with Hurricanes', first appeared in *Red Beans* by Victor Hernandez Cruz, Copyright © 1991 by Victor Hernandez Cruz; the author, Jeni Couzyn for 'Spell to Summon the Owner of the Shoes' from *House of Changes*; EMI Songs Ltd for 'Track Suit' from *Ten Years in an Open Necked Shirt* by John Cooper Clarke © 1983; Faber & Faber Ltd for 'Night Mail' from *Collected Poems* by W. H. Auden edited by Edward Mendelson, 'Message' from *Making Cocoa for Kingsley Amis* by Wendy Cope, 'The Names of the Hare' by Seamus Heaney from *The Rattle Bag* edited by Seamus Heaney and Ted Hughes, 'Leaves' from *Season Songs* by Ted Hughes, 'Prayer Before Birth' from *Collected Poems* by Louis MacNeice edited by E. R. Dobbs, 'Bodywork' from *Dragonsfire and Other Poems* by Judith Nicholls, 'A Many-Spendoured Doughnut' from *Words on a Faded T-shirt* by Norman Silver; the authors' agents on behalf of Eleanor and Herbert Farjeon for 'Lady Godiva' from *Heroes and Heroines* (J M Dent); Farrar, Straus & Giroux, Inc and North Point Press for 'Chant of a Rock' from *Break the Mirror* by Nanao Sakaki, Copyright © 1987 by Nanao Sakaki; Farrar, Straus & Giroux, Inc/William Peter Kosmas for 'School' from *Collected Poems* by Federico Garcia Lorca and edited by Christopher Maurer. Translation copyright © 1991 by Herederos de Federica Garcia Lorca and Jerome Rothenberg. All rights reserved. For information regarding rights and permissions for works by Federico Garcia Lorca, please contact William Peter Kosmas, Esq., 77 Rodney Court, 6/8 Miada Vale, London W9 1TJ; 57 Productions for 'Brief Encounter' by Ann Ziety first published in *The Popular Front of Contemporary Poetry* (Apples & Snakes, 1992); Forest Books for 'Don't ask me' from *Through the Needle's Eye* by Jon Milos translated by Brenda Walker; the author, Martin Glynn for 'Machoman'; HarperCollins Publishers/author's agent on behalf of the Estate of Raymond Carver for 'The Car' from *In a Marine Light* (UK title)/*Ultramarine* (US title) Copyright (c) 1986 by Raymond Carver. Copyright renewed 1993 by Tess Gallagher. Reprinted by permission of International Creative Management Inc; Henry Holt & Company Inc for 'I am a purse. . .' from *Yevgeny Yevtushenko: The Collected Poems, 1952-1990* edited by Albert C. Todd with Yevgeny Yevtushenko and James Ragan, Copyright © 1991 by Henry Holt and Company Inc; the author, Amryl Johnson for 'Granny in de Market Place' from *Tread Carefully in Paradise* (Cofa Press, 1991); the author, June Jordan for 'What Is This In Reference To?'; the author, Jackie Kay for 'New Baby', first appeared in *Two's Company* (Blackie) and now reprinted by Puffin; Jay Landesman, Publishers for 'Jaywalkin' by Fran Landesman; the author, Bill Lewis for 'Riddle Song'; KLJ Records Ltd for 'Reggae

Addison Wesley Longman Limited
Edinburgh Gate, Harlow,
Essex CM20 2JE, England
and Associated Companies throughout the world

Longman Group Limited 1995
All rights reserved; no part of this publication may be reproduced,
stored in a retrieval system, or transmitted in any form or by any means,
electronic, mechanical, photocopying, recording, or otherwise without either the
prior written permission of the Publishers or a licence permitting
restricted copying issued by the Copyright Licensing Agency Ltd,
90 Tottenham Court Road, London W1P 9HE.

This educational edition first published 1995
ISBN 0 582 22587 6
Third impression 1998

Editorial material set in Minion 10.5/12
Printed in Singapore through Addison Wesley Longman China Limited

Illustration by John Clementson

The publisher's policy is to use paper manufactured from sustainable forests.

Consultants: Geoff Barton and Jackie Head

Longman Literature
Series editor: Roy Blatchford

Short stories

Angelou, Goodison,
  Senior & Walker   *Quartet of Stories*   0 582 28730 8
Thomas Hardy   *The Wessex Tales*   0 582 25405 1
Susan Hill   *A Bit of Singing and Dancing*   0 582 09711 8
George Layton   *A Northern Childhood*   0 582 25404 3
                Twisters: stories from other centuries   0 582 29253 0

Poetry

Poems from Other Centuries   edited by Adrian Tissier   0 582 22585 X
Poems in my Earphone   collected by John Agard   0 582 22587 6
Poems One   edited by Celeste Flower   0 582 25400 0
Poems Two   edited by Paul Jordan & Julia Markus   0 582 25401 9
Voices of the Great War   edited by Geoff Barton   0 582 29248 4

Plays

Alan Ayckbourn   *Absent Friends*   0 582 30242 0
Ad de Bont   *Mirad. A Boy from Bosnia*   0 582 24949 X
Oliver Goldsmith   *She Stoops to Conquer*   0 582 25397 7
Henrik Ibsen   *Three plays: The Wild Duck, Ghosts and A Doll's House*   0 582 24948 1
Ben Jonson   *Volpone*   0 582 25408 6
Christopher Marlowe   *Doctor Faustus*   0 582 25409 4
Terence Rattigan   *The Winslow Boy*   0 582 06019 2
Jack Rosenthal   *Wide-Eyed and Legless*   0 582 24950 3
Willy Russell   *Educating Rita*   0 582 06013 3
                Shirley Valentine   0 582 08173 4
Peter Shaffer   *Equus*   0 582 09712 6
                The Royal Hunt of the Sun   0 582 06014 1
Bernard Shaw   *Androcles and the Lion*   0 582 29252 2
                Arms and the Man   0 582 07785 0
                The Devil's Disciple   0 582 25410 8
                Pygmalion   0 582 06015 X
                Saint Joan   0 582 07786 9
R B Sheridan   *The Rivals* and *The School for Scandal*   0 582 25396 9
J Webster   *The Duchess of Malfi*   0 582 28731 6
Oscar Wilde   *The Importance of Being Earnest*   0 582 07784 2

Other titles in the Longman Literature series are listed on page ii.